Glencoe McGraw-Hill

# Math Connects
### Course 1

## Chapter 1
## Resource Masters

**Consumable Workbooks** Many of the worksheets contained in the Chapter Resource Masters are available as consumable workbooks in both English and Spanish.

|  | MHID | ISBN |
|---|---|---|
| *Study Guide and Intervention Workbook* | 0-07-881032-9 | 978-0-07-881032-9 |
| *Skills Practice Workbook* | 0-07-881031-0 | 978-0-07-881031-2 |
| *Practice Workbook* | 0-07-881034-5 | 978-0-07-881034-3 |
| *Word Problem Practice Workbook* | 0-07-881033-7 | 978-0-07-881033-6 |

**Spanish Versions**

|  | MHID | ISBN |
|---|---|---|
| *Study Guide and Intervention Workbook* | 0-07-881036-1 | 978-0-07-881036-7 |
| *Skills Practice Workbook* | 0-07-881035-3 | 978-0-07-881035-0 |
| *Practice Workbook* | 0-07-881038-8 | 978-0-07-881038-1 |
| *Word Problem Practice Workbook* | 0-07-881037-X | 978-0-07-881037-4 |

**Answers for Workbooks** The answers for Chapter 1 of these workbooks can be found in the back of this Chapter Resource Masters booklet.

**StudentWorks Plus™** This CD-ROM includes the entire Student Edition test along with the English workbooks listed above.

**TeacherWorks Plus™** All of the materials found in this booklet are included for viewing, printing, and editing in this CD-ROM.

**Spanish Assessment Masters** (MHID: 0-07-881039-6, ISBN: 978-0-07-881039-8) These masters contain a Spanish version of Chapter 1 Test Form 2A and Form 2C.

 **Glencoe**

The **McGraw-Hill** Companies

Send all inquiries to:
Glencoe/McGraw-Hill
8787 Orion Place
Columbus, OH 43240

ISBN: 978-0-07-881017-6
MHID: 0-07-881017-5

Printed in the United States of America.

2 3 4  5 6 7 8 9 10 047 16 15 14 13 12 11 10 09 08

*Math Connects, Course 1*

# CONTENTS

# Teacher's Guide to Using the
# *Chapter 1 Resource Masters*

The *Chapter 1 Resource Masters* includes the core materials needed for Chapter 1. These materials include worksheets, extensions, and assessment options. The answers for these pages appear at the back of this booklet.

All of the materials found in this booklet are included for viewing and printing on the *TeacherWorks Plus™* CD-ROM.

## Chapter Resources

*Student-Built Glossary* (pages 1–2) These masters are a student study tool that presents up to twenty of the key vocabulary terms from the chapter. Students are to record definitions and/or examples for each term. You may suggest that students highlight or star the terms with which they are not familiar. Give this to students before beginning Lesson 1-1. Encourage them to add these pages to their mathematics study notebooks. Remind them to complete the appropriate words as they study each lesson.

*Family Letter and Family Activity* (pages 3–6) The letter informs your students' families of the mathematics they will be learning in this chapter. The family activity helps them to practice problems that are similar to those on the state test. A full solution for each problem is included. Spanish versions of these pages are also included. Give these to students to take home before beginning the chapter.

*Anticipation Guide* (pages 7–8) This master, presented in both English and Spanish, is a survey used before beginning the chapter to pinpoint what students may or may not know about the concepts in the chapter. Students will revisit this survey after they complete the chapter to see if their perceptions have changed.

## Lesson Resources

*Lesson Reading Guide* Get Ready for the Lesson reiterates the questions from the beginning of the Student Edition lesson. Read the Lesson asks students to interpret the context of and relationships among terms in the lesson. Finally, Remember What You Learned asks students to summarize what they have learned using various representation techniques. Use as a study tool for note taking or as an informal reading assignment. It is also a helpful tool for ELL (English Language Learners).

*Study Guide and Intervention* This master provides vocabulary, key concepts, additional worked-out examples and Check Your Progress exercises to use as a reteaching activity. It can also be used in conjunction with the Student Edition as an instructional tool for students who have been absent.

*Skills Practice* This master focuses more on the computational nature of the lesson. Use as an additional practice option or as homework for second-day teaching of the lesson.

*Practice* This master closely follows the types of problems found in the Exercises section of the Student Edition and includes word problems. Use as an additional practice option or as homework for second-day teaching of the lesson.

**Word Problem Practice** This master includes additional practice in solving word problems that apply the concepts of the lesson. Use as an additional practice or as homework for second-day teaching of the lesson.

**Enrichment** These activities may extend the concepts of the lesson, offer a historical or multicultural look at the concepts, or widen students' perspectives on the mathematics they are learning. They are written for use with all levels of students.

**Graphing Calculator, Scientific Calculator, or Spreadsheet Activities** These activities present ways in which technology can be used with the concepts in some lessons of this chapter. Use as an alternative approach to some concepts or as an integral part of your lesson presentation.

## Assessment Options

The assessment masters in the *Chapter 1 Resource Masters* offer a wide range of assessment tools for formative (monitoring) assessment and summative (final) assessment.

**Student Recording Sheet** This master corresponds with the Test Practice at the end of the chapter.

**Extended-Response Rubric** This master provides information for teachers and students on how to assess performance on open-ended questions.

**Quizzes** Four free-response quizzes offer assessment at appropriate intervals in the chapter.

**Mid-Chapter Test** This 1-page test provides an option to assess the first half of the chapter. It parallels the timing of the Mid-Chapter Quiz in the Student Edition and includes both multiple-choice and free-response questions.

**Vocabulary Test** This test is suitable for all students. It includes a list of vocabulary words and 10 questions to assess students' knowledge of those words. This can also be used in conjunction with one of the leveled chapter tests.

## Leveled Chapter Tests

- *Form 1* contains multiple-choice questions and is intended for use with below grade level students.

- *Forms 2A and 2B* contain multiple-choice questions aimed at on grade level students. These tests are similar in format to offer comparable testing situations.

- *Forms 2C and 2D* contain free-response questions aimed at on grade level students. These tests are similar in format to offer comparable testing situations.

- *Form 3* is a free-response test for use with above grade level students.

All of the above mentioned tests include a free-response Bonus question.

**Extended-Response Test** Performance assessment tasks are suitable for all students. Samples answers and a scoring rubric are included for evaluation.

**Standardized Test Practice** These three pages are cumulative in nature. It includes two parts: multiple-choice questions with bubble-in answer format and short-answer free-response questions.

## Answers

- The answers for the Anticipation Guide and Lesson Resources are provided as reduced pages with answers appearing in red.

- Full-size answer keys are provided for the assessment masters.

## 1 Student-Built Glossary

This is an alphabetical list of new vocabulary terms you will learn in Chapter 1. As you study the chapter, complete each term's definition or description. Remember to add the page number where you found the term. Add this page to your math study notebook to review vocabulary at the end of the chapter.

| Vocabulary Term | Found on Page | Definition/Description/Example |
|---|---|---|
| algebra [AL-juh-bruh] | | |
| algebraic [AL-juh-BRAY-ihk] expression | | |
| area | | |
| base | | |
| composite [com-PAH-zit] number | | |
| cubed | | |
| equals sign | | |
| equation [ih-KWAY-zhuhn] | | |
| evaluate | | |
| exponent [ex-SPOH-nuhnt] | | |
| factor | | |

## 1 Student-Built Glossary *(continued)*

| Vocabulary Term | Found on Page | Definition/Description/Example |
|---|---|---|
| formula<br>[FOR-myuh-luh] | | |
| function [FUNK-shuhn] | | |
| function table | | |
| function rule | | |
| numerical expression | | |
| order of operations | | |
| power | | |
| prime factorization | | |
| prime number | | |
| solution | | |
| solve | | |
| squared | | |
| variable<br>[VAIR-ee-uh-buhl] | | |

**1** **Family Letter**

Dear Parent or Guardian:

Students are often frustrated in math classes because they do not see how they can use the material in the real world. In our math class, however, we try to take mathematics beyond the classroom to a point where students realize and appreciate its importance in their daily lives.

In **Chapter 1, Algebra: Number Patterns and Functions**, your child will be learning about problem solving, patterns, prime factors, the order of operations, variables and expressions, and powers and exponents. Your child will also solve equations and find the area of rectangles. In the study of this chapter, your child will complete a variety of daily classroom assignments and activities and possibly produce a chapter project.

By signing this letter and returning it with your child, you agree to encourage your child by getting involved. Enclosed is an activity you can do with your child that practices how the math we will be learning in Chapter 1 might be tested. You may also wish to log on to **glencoe.com** for self-check quizzes and other study help. If you have any questions or comments, feel free to contact me at school.

Sincerely,

Signature of Parent or Guardian _____ Date _____

## 1 Family Activity

### State Test Practice

**Fold the page along the dashed line. Work each problem on another piece of paper. Then unfold the page to check your work.**

1. For the table below, find the expression that can be used to find term $n$ in the sequence. Which expression can be used to find $n$?

| Position, $n$ | Value of Term |
|:---:|:---:|
| 1 | 6 |
| 2 | 8 |
| 3 | 10 |
| 4 | 12 |
| 5 | 14 |
| $n$ | ? |

**A** $3n + 2$      **C** $2n + 4$

**B** $2n - 2$      **D** $2n + 3$

2. What is the prime factorization for 125?

     **A** $5 \times 25$

     **B** $5^3$

     **C** $12 \times 5$

     **D** $3^5$

*Fold here.*

- - - - - - - - - - - - - - - - - - - - - - - - - - - - - - - - - - - - - - - - - - - - - - - - - - - - - - - - -

**Solution**

1. *Hint: Remember to test at least three of the number pairs in the expressions before deciding on an answer. Some expressions may work for one of the pairs, but not all of them.*

While $3n + 2$ will work for the second pair ($3 \times 2 + 2 = 8$), it does not work with the rest of the number pairs (For example: $3 \times 1 + 2 \neq 6$).

$2n - 2$ and $2n + 3$ do not work for any of the pairs.

The expression that does work for all of them is $2n + 4$. This is modeled below:

$$2 \times 1 + 4 = 6$$
$$2 \times 2 + 4 = 8$$
$$2 \times 3 + 4 = 10$$
$$2 \times 4 + 4 = 12$$
$$2 \times 5 + 4 = 14$$

The answer is **C.**

**Solution**

2. *Hint: Prime factorization is the expression of a number as the product of prime numbers. A prime number is a number that is divisible only by one and itself.*

Both **A** and **C** are wrong because they contain numbers that are not prime.

If you find the value of the remaining two choices, you will find that **B** ($5^3 = 5 \times 5 \times 5$) equals 125 while **D** ($3^5 = 3 \times 3 \times 3 \times 3 \times 3$) equals 243.

The answer is **B.**

# 1 Carta a la familia

**Estimado padre o apoderado:**

A menudo, los alumnos se sienten decepcionados en las clases de matemáticas por no saber cómo aplicarlas en la vida real. En nuestra clase, sin embargo, intentamos proyectar las matemáticas fuera del aula hasta lograr que los alumnos perciban y aprecien su importancia en la vida cotidiana.

En el **Capítulo 1, Álgebra patrones numéricos y funciones**, su hijo(a) aprenderá sobre solución de problemas, patrones, factores primos, el orden de las operaciones, variables y expresiones; y potencias y exponentes. Su hijo(a) también resolverá ecuaciones y calculará el área de rectángulos. En el estudio de este capítulo, su hijo(a) completará una variedad de tareas y actividades diarias y es posible que trabaje en un proyecto del capítulo.

Al firmar esta carta y devolverla con su hijo(a), usted se compromete a ayudarlo(a) a participar en su aprendizaje. Junto con esta carta, va incluida una actividad que puede realizar con él(ella) y la cual practica lo que podrían encontrar en las pruebas de los conceptos matemáticos que aprenderán en el Capítulo 1. Además, visiten **glencoe.com** para ver autocontroles y otras ayudas para el estudio. Si tiene cualquier pregunta o comentario, por favor contácteme en la escuela.

Cordialmente,

Firma del padre o apoderado _____ Fecha _____

# 1 Actividad en familia

## Práctica para la prueba estatal

**Doblen la página a lo largo de las líneas punteadas. Resuelvan cada problema en otra hoja de papel. Luego, desdoblen la página y revisen las respuestas.**

**1.** En la tabla siguiente, busca la expresión que pueda usarse para calcular el término $n$ en la sucesión. ¿Qué expresión puede usarse para despejar $n$?

| Posición, $n$ | Valor del término |
|:---:|:---:|
| 1 | 6 |
| 2 | 8 |
| 3 | 10 |
| 4 | 12 |
| 5 | 14 |
| $n$ | ? |

**A** $3n + 2$

**B** $2n - 2$

**C** $2n + 4$

**D** $2n + 3$

**2.** ¿Cuál es el factor primo de 125?

**A** $5 \times 25$

**B** $5^3$

**C** $12 \times 5$

**D** $3^5$

*Fold here.*

- - - - - - - - - - - - - - - - - - - - - - - - - - - - - - - - - - - - - - - - - - - - - - - - - - - - - - -

## Solución

**1.** *Ayuda: Recuerden probar por lo menos tres pares de números en las expresiones antes de seleccionar la respuesta. Algunas expresiones se aplican a alguno de los pares, pero no a todos.*

Aunque $3n + 2$ funciona con el segundo par ($3 \times 2 + 2 = 8$), no funciona con el resto de los pares. (Por ejemplo: $3 \times 1 + 2 \neq 6$).

$2n - 2$ y $2n + 3$ no funcionan con ninguno de los pares.

La expresión que sí funciona con todos es $2n + 4$. Esto se muestra a continuación:

$$2 \times 1 + 4 = 6$$
$$2 \times 2 + 4 = 8$$
$$2 \times 3 + 4 = 10$$
$$2 \times 4 + 4 = 12$$
$$2 \times 5 + 4 = 14$$

La respuesta es **C.**

## Solución

**2.** *Ayuda: La factorización prima es expresar un número como el producto de números primos. Un número primo es un número divisible entre uno solamente y entre sí mismo.*

Tanto **A** como **C** son incorrectos por contener números no primos.

Si calculas el valor de las dos selecciones restantes se tiene que
**B** ($5^3 = 5 \times 5 \times 5$) es igual a 125 mientras que
**D** ($3^5 = 3 \times 3 \times 3 \times 3 \times 3$) es igual a 243.

La respuesta es **B.**

# 1  Anticipation Guide

## Algebra: Number Patterns and Functions

Chapter Resources

**STEP 1**   *Before you begin Chapter 1*

- Read each statement.
- Decide whether you Agree (A) or Disagree (D) with the statement.
- Write A or D in the first column OR if you are not sure whether you agree or disagree, write NS (Not Sure).

| STEP 1 A, D, or NS | Statement | STEP 2 A or D |
|---|---|---|
| | **1.** An estimate is not a good indication of the answer to a problem because an estimate is not the exact answer. | |
| | **2.** To determine when an estimate can be used to answer a problem, look for words such as "about" that indicate an exact answer is not needed. | |
| | **3.** A prime number is any number with more than two factors. | |
| | **4.** $4^1$ and 4 are equivalent. | |
| | **5.** A number to the second power, such as $7^2$, is said to be *squared*. | |
| | **6.** In using the order of operations to simplify an expression, all addition and subtraction should be done first. | |
| | **7.** In using the order of operations to simplify an expression, multiply and divide in order from left to right. | |
| | **8.** In the expression $3x + 4$, $x$ is called a *variable*. | |
| | **9.** Using a guess and check strategy to solve a math problem is never a good idea. | |
| | **10.** To solve the equation $t - 5 = 12$, subtract 5 from 12. | |
| | **11.** The area of a rectangle is found by multiplying the length by the width. | |
| | **12.** The dimensions of a rectangle with an area of 12 square units must be 4 and 3. | |

**STEP 2**   *After you complete Chapter 1*

- Reread each statement and complete the last column by entering an A (Agree) or a D (Disagree).
- Did any of your opinions about the statements change from the first column?
- For those statements that you mark with a D, use a separate sheet of paper to explain why you disagree. Use examples, if possible.

# 1 Ejercicios preparatorios

## Álgebra: patrones numéricos y funciones

**PASO 1** *Antes de comenzar el Capítulo 1*

- Lee cada enunciado.

- Decide si estás de acuerdo (A) o en desacuerdo (D) con el enunciado.

- Escribe A o D en la primera columna O si no estás seguro(a) de la respuesta, escribe NS (No estoy seguro(a)).

| PASO 1 A, D o NS | Enunciado | PASO 2 A o D |
|---|---|---|
| | **1.** Una estimación no es una buena indicación de la respuesta a un problema porque una estimación no es la respuesta exacta. | |
| | **2.** Para determinar cuándo puede usarse una estimación para resolver un problema, busca palabras como "aproximadamente", las cuales indican que no se necesita una respuesta exacta. | |
| | **3.** Un número primo es cualquier número con más de dos factores. | |
| | **4.** $4^1$ y 4 son equivalentes. | |
| | **5.** Un número elevado a la segunda potencia, como $7^2$, se dice que está al cuadrado. | |
| | **6.** Al reducir una expresión usando el orden de las operaciones, se deben hacer primero todas las adiciones y sustracciones. | |
| | **7.** Al reducir una expresión usando el orden de las operaciones, multiplica y divide ordenadamente de izquierda a derecha. | |
| | **8.** En la expresión $3x + 4$, a $x$ se le denomina variable. | |
| | **9.** Nunca es buena idea usar la estrategia de adivinar y verificar para resolver un problema matemático. | |
| | **10.** Para resolver la ecuación $t - 5 = 12$, sustrae 5 de 12. | |
| | **11.** El área de un rectángulo se obtiene al multiplicar el largo por el ancho. | |
| | **12.** Las dimensiones de un rectángulo con un área de 12 unidades cuadradas deben ser 4 y 3. | |

**PASO 2** *Después de completar el Capítulo 1*

- Vuelve a leer cada enunciado y completa la última columna con una A o una D.

- ¿Cambió cualquiera de tus opiniones sobre los enunciados de la primera columna?

- En una hoja de papel aparte, escribe un ejemplo de por qué estás en desacuerdo con los enunciados que marcaste con una D.

## 1-1 Lesson Reading Guide

### A Plan for Problem Solving

## Get Ready for the Lesson

**Read the introduction at the top of page 24 in your textbook. Write your answers below.**

**1.** How many purple and yellow beads are used to make one necklace?

**2.** How many purple and yellow beads will be needed to make all eight necklaces?

**3.** Explain how you found the number of each color of beads needed to make all eight necklaces.

## Read the Lesson

**4.** Why do you think understanding the problem is so important to finding the solution? **Sample answer: You need to understand what you are looking for so that you can find the correct solution.**

**5.** Relate the plan step of the problem solving strategy to preparing for a trip. **Sample answer: Before going on a trip you must plan how you are going to get there, what you must pack, how long you will be gone, etc.**

**6.** In the four-step plan for problem solving, think about the term *check*. Does *check* come before or after the solution? (*Hint:* What are you checking?)

## Remember What You Learned

**7.** Think about the four steps in the problem-solving plan: Understand, Plan, Solve, Check. Write a sentence about something you like to help you remember the four words. For example, "I understand how to play chess."

**Lesson 1-1**

## 1-1 Study Guide and Intervention

### A Plan for Problem Solving

When solving problems, it is helpful to have an organized plan to solve the problem. The following four steps can be used to solve any math problem.

**1 Understand** – Read and get a general understanding of the problem.

**2 Plan** – Make a plan to solve the problem and estimate the solution.

**3 Solve** – Use your plan to solve the problem.

**4 Check** – Check the reasonableness of your solution.

**Example 1** SPORTS **The table shows the number of field goals made by Henry High School's top three basketball team members during last year's season. How many more field goals did Brad make than Denny?**

| Name | 3-Point Field Goals |
| --- | --- |
| Brad | 216 |
| Chris | 201 |
| Denny | 195 |

**Understand** You know the number of field goals made. You need to find how many more field goals Brad made than Denny.

**Plan** Use only the needed information, the goals made by Brad and Denny. To find the difference, subtract 195 from 216.

**Solve** $216 - 195 = 21$; Brad made 21 more field goals than Denny.

**Check** Check the answer by adding. Since $195 + 21 = 216$, the answer is correct.

### Exercises

1. During which step do you check your work to make sure your answer is correct?

2. Explain what you do during the first step of the problem-solving plan.

**SPORTS For Exercises 3 and 4, use the field goal table above and the four-step plan.**

3. How many more field goals did Chris make than Denny?

4. How many field goals did the three boys make all together?

## 1-1  Skills Practice

### *A Plan for Problem Solving*

**Use the four-step plan to solve each problem.**

1. **GEOGRAPHY** The president is going on a campaign trip to California, first flying about 2,840 miles from Washington, D.C., to San Francisco and then another 390 to Los Angeles before returning the 2,650 miles back to the capital. How many miles will the president have flown?

2. **POPULATION** In 1990, the total population of Sacramento, CA, was 369,365. In 2000, its population was 407,018. How much did the population increase?

3. **MONEY** The Palmer family wants to purchase a DVD player in four equal installments of $64. What is the cost of the DVD player?

4. **COMMERCIALS** The highest average cost of a 30-second commercial in October, 2002 was $455,700. How much was this commercial worth per second?

5. **SPORTS** A tennis tournament starts with 16 people. The number in each round is shown in the table. How many players will be in the 4th round?

| 1st Round | 16 |
|-----------|----|
| 2nd Round | 8  |
| 3rd Round | 4  |
| 4th Round | ?  |

**Complete the pattern.**

6. 2, 4, 8, 16, 32, ___

7. 16, 19, 22, 25, 28, 31, ___

8. 81, 72, 63, 54, ___

9. 5, 15, 20, 30, 35, 45, 50, ___

10. 50, 40, 45, 35, 40, 30, 35, ___, ___, ___, ___

11. 6, 12, 18, ___, ___, ___, ___

## 1-1 Practice

### A Plan for Problem Solving

**PATTERNS** Complete each pattern.

**1.** 17, 21, 25, 29, _____, _____, _____,

**2.** 32, 29, 26, 23, _____, _____, _____,

**3.** 1, 2, 4, 7, _____, _____, _____,

**4.** 64, 32, 16, 8, _____, _____, _____,

**5.** **ANALYZE GRAPHS** Refer to the graph. How many acres smaller is Lake Meredith National Recreation Area than Big Thicket National Preserve?

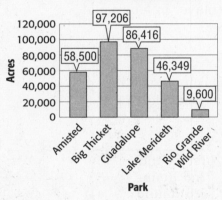

**Sizes of National Parks**

**6.** **TRAVEL** The distance between Dallas and Beaumont is about 290 miles. Henry drove from Dallas to Beaumont at 58 miles per hour. How many hours did it take Henry to reach Beaumont?

**7.** **ANALYZE TABLES** The table lists the times that ferries leave the terminal every day. At what times will the next three ferries leave the terminal?

| 6:36 A.M. |
| 7:11 A.M. |
| 7:17 A.M. |
| 7:52 A.M. |
| 7:58 A.M. |

**8.** **MONEY** The Wilsons bought a refrigerator and a stove for a total cost of $745. They will pay for the purchase in five equal payments. What will be the amount of each payment?

**9.** **MUSIC** Luanda practices playing the piano for 24 minutes each day. How many hours does she practice in one year?

## 1-1  Word Problem Practice

### A Plan for Problem Solving

Use the four-step plan to solve each problem.

**GEOGRAPHY** For Exercises 1 and 2, use the poster information about Crater Lake National Park in Oregon.

| Visit Crater Lake National Park |
|---|
| 90 miles of trails |
| 26 miles of shoreline |
| Boat tours available |
| Open 24 hours |
| |
| Directions from Klamath Falls: Take U.S. Highway 97 north 21 miles, then go west on S.R. 62 for 29 miles. |

1. How many more miles of trails are there than miles of shoreline in Crater Lake National Park?

2. How many miles is it from Klamath Falls to Crater Lake National Park?

3. **SPORTS** Jasmine swims 12 laps every afternoon, Monday through Friday. How many laps does she swim in one week?

4. **SPORTS** Samantha can run one mile in 8 minutes. At this rate, how long will it take for her to run 5 miles?

5. **SPORTS** On a certain day, 525 people signed up to play softball. If 15 players are assigned to each team, how many teams can be formed?

6. **PATTERNS** Complete the pattern: 5, 7, 10, 14, ___, ___, ___

7. **SHOPPING** Josita received $50 as a gift. She plans to buy two cassette tapes that cost $9 each and a headphone set that costs $25. How much money will she have left?

8. **BUS SCHEDULE** A bus stops at the corner of Elm Street and Oak Street every half hour between 9 A.M. and 3 P.M. and every 15 minutes between 3 P.M. and 6 P.M. How many times will a bus stop at the corner between 9 A.M. and 6 P.M.?

## 1-1  Enrichment

### Using a Reference Point

There are many times when you need to make an estimate in relation to a *reference point*. For example, at the right there are prices listed for some school supplies. You might wonder if $5 is enough money to buy a small spiral notebook and a pen. This is how you might estimate, using $5 as the reference point.

- The notebook costs $1.59 and the pen costs $3.69.
- $1 + $3 = $4. I have $5 − $4, or $1, left.
- $0.59 and $0.69 are each more than $0.50, so $0.59 + $0.69 is more than $1.

So $5 will not be enough money.

**Use the prices at the right to answer each question.**

1. Jamaal has $5. Will that be enough money to buy a large spiral notebook and a pack of pencils?

2. Andreas wants to buy a three-ring binder and two packs of filler paper. Will $7 be enough money?

3. Rosita has $10. Can she buy a large spiral notebook and a pen and still have $5 left?

4. Kevin has $10 and has to buy a pen and two small spiral notebooks. Will he have $2.50 left to buy lunch?

5. What is the greatest number of erasers you can buy with $2?

6. What is the greatest amount of filler paper that you can buy with $5?

7. Lee bought three items and spent exactly $8.99. What were the items?

8. Select five items whose total cost is as close as possible to $10, but not more than $10.

Spiral Notebook
Large $2.29
Small $1.59

Three-Ring
Binder
$4.75

Filler Paper
Pack of 100
$1.29

Ball-Point
Pen
$3.69

Pencils
Pack of 10
$2.39

Eraser
$0.55

## 1-2  Lesson Reading Guide

### *Prime Factors*

### Get Ready for the Lesson

**Complete the Mini Lab at the top of page 28 in your textbook. Write your answers below.**

**1.** For what numbers can more than one rectangle be formed?

**2.** For what numbers can only one rectangle be formed?

**3.** For the numbers in which only one rectangle is formed, what do you notice about the dimensions of the rectangle?

### Read the Lesson

**4.** The word *factorization* is made up of *factor* + a verb ending + a noun ending. Write a definition for each of the following mathematical terms:

**a.** factor

**b.** to factorize, or to factor

**c.** factorization

**5.** Is 9 a prime number or a composite number? Explain.

### Remember What You Learned

**6.** Pick a number that has two or three digits. Explain to someone else how to use a factor tree to find the prime factors of the number. In your explanation, show how the rules of divisibility help you to do the factoring.

Lesson 1-2

## 1-2 Study Guide and Intervention

### Prime Factors

Factors are the numbers that are multiplied to get a product. A product is the answer to a multiplication problem. A **prime number** is a whole number that has only 2 factors, 1 and the number itself. A **composite number** is a number greater than 1 with more than two factors.

**Example 1** Tell whether each number is *prime*, *composite*, or *neither*.

| Number | Factors | Prime or Composite? |
|--------|---------|---------------------|
| 15 | 1 × 15<br>3 × 5 | Composite |
| 17 | 1 × 17 | Prime |
| 1 | 1 | Neither |

**Example 2** Find the prime factorization of 18.

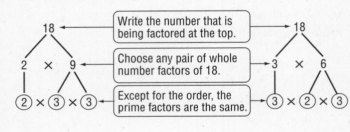

18 is divisible by 2, because the ones digit is divisible by 2.
Circle the prime number, 2.
9 is divisible by 3, because the sum of the digits is divisible by 3.
Circle the prime numbers, 3 and 3.
The prime factorization of 18 is 2 × 3 × 3.

### Exercises

Tell whether each number is *prime*, *composite*, or *neither*.

1. 7                2. 12               3. 29

4. 81               5. 18               6. 23

7. 54               8. 28               9. 120

10. 243             11. 61              12. 114

Find the prime factorization of each number.

13. 125                          14. 44

15. 11                           16. 56

## 1-2 Skills Practice

### Prime Factors

**Tell whether each number is *prime*, *composite*, or *neither*.**

1. 0                2. 1                3. 2                4. 3

5. 4                6. 5                7. 6                8. 7

9. 8                10. 9               11. 10              12. 11

**Find the prime factorization of each number.**

13. 9                           14. 25

15. 28                          16. 54

17. 34                          18. 72

19. 55                          20. 63

**SCHOOL** For Exercises 21–24, use the table below.

| Marisa's History Test Scores | |
| --- | --- |
| Date | Test Score |
| January 28 | 67 |
| February 15 | 81 |
| March 5 | 97 |
| March 29 | 100 |

21. Which test scores are prime numbers?

22. Which prime number is the least prime number?

23. Find the prime factorization of 100.

24. Find the prime factorization of 81.

Lesson 1–2

## 1-2 Practice

### *Prime Factors*

**Tell whether each number is *prime*, *composite*, or *neither*.**

**1.** 24          **2.** 1          **3.** 13          **4.** 25

**5.** 91          **6.** 0          **7.** 181          **8.** 145

**Find the prime factorization of each number.**

**9.** 16          **10.** 48          **11.** 66

**12.** 56          **13.** 80          **14.** 95

**15.** Find the least prime number that is greater than 50.

**16.** All odd numbers greater than 7 can be expressed as the sum of three prime numbers. Which three prime numbers have a sum of 43? Justify your answer.

**17. GARDENING** Julia wants to plant 24 tomato plants in rows. Each row will have the same number of plants in it. Find three possible numbers of rows and the number of plants in each row.

**18. SHOPPING** Jamal bought boxes of nails that each cost the same. He spent a total of $42. Find three possible costs per box and the number of boxes that he could have purchased.

## 1-2   Word Problem Practice

### Prime Factors

**ANIMALS** For Exercises 1–3, use the table that shows the height and weight of caribou.

| CARIBOU | Height at the Shoulder | | Weight | |
|---|---|---|---|---|
| | inches | centimeters | pounds | kilograms |
| Cows (females) | 43 | 107 | 220 | 99 |
| Bulls (males) | 50 | 125 | 400 | 180 |

1. Which animal heights and weights are prime numbers?

2. Write the weight of caribou cows in kilograms as a prime factorization.

3. **ANIMALS** Caribou calves weigh about 13 pounds at birth. Tell whether this weight is a prime or a composite number.

4. **SPEED** A wildlife biologist once found a caribou traveling at 37 miles per hour. Tell whether this speed is a prime or composite number. Explain.

5. **GEOMETRY** To find the area of a floor, you can multiply its length times its width. The measure of the area of a floor is 49. Find the most likely length and width of the room.

6. **GEOMETRY** To find the volume of a box, you can multiply its height, width, and length. The measure of the volume of a box is 70. Find its possible dimensions.

Lesson 1-2

## 1-2 Enrichment

## Making Models for Numbers

Have you wondered why we read the number $3^2$ as three squared?
The reason is that a common model for $3^2$ is a square with sides of
length 3 units. As you see, the figure that results is made up of
9 square units.

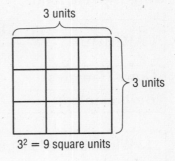

3 units

3 units

$3^2$ = 9 square units

**Make a model for each expression.**

1. $2^2$       2. $4^2$       3. $1^2$       4. $5^2$

Since we read the expression $2^3$ as *two cubed*, you
probably have guessed that there is also a model for
this number. The model, shown at the right, is a cube
with sides of length 2 units. The figure that results
is made up of 8 *cubic units*.

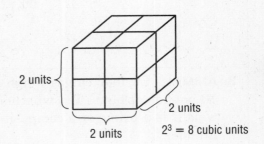

2 units

2 units

2 units       $2^3$ = 8 cubic units

**Exercises 5 and 6 refer to the figure at the right.**

5. What expression is being modeled?

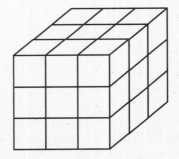

6. Suppose that the entire cube is painted red. Then
   the cube is cut into small cubes along the lines shown.

   a. How many small cubes are there in all?

   b. How many small cubes have red paint on exactly
      three of their faces?

   c. How many small cubes have red paint on
      exactly two of their faces?

   d. How many small cubes have red paint on
      exactly one face?

   e. How many small cubes have no red paint at all?

7. **CHALLENGE** In the space at the right, draw a model
   for the expression $4^3$.

## 1-3  Lesson Reading Guide

### Powers and Exponents

### Get Ready for the Lesson

**Complete the Mini Lab at the top of page 32 in your textbook. Write your answers below.**

1. What prime factors did you record?

2. How does the number of folds relate to the number of factors in the prime factorization of the number of holes?

3. Write the prime factorization of the number of holes made if you folded it eight times.

### Read the Lesson

4. Describe the expression $2^5$. In your description, use the terms *power*, *base*, and *exponent*.

5. In the power $3^5$, what does the exponent 5 indicate?

6. Complete the following table.

| Expression | Words |
|---|---|
| $4^3$ | |
| $7^2$ | |
| $9^6$ | |
| $8 \times 8 \times 8 \times 8$ | |
| $3 \times 3 \times 3 \times 3 \times 3$ | |

### Remember What You Learned

7. Explain how to find the value of $5^4$.

Lesson 1-3

## 1-3   Study Guide and Intervention

### Powers and Exponents

A product of prime factors can be written using exponents and a base. Numbers expressed using exponents are called **powers**.

| Powers | Words | Expression | Value |
|--------|-------|------------|-------|
| $4^2$ | 4 to the second power or 4 squared | $4 \times 4$ | 16 |
| $5^6$ | 5 to the sixth power | $5 \times 5 \times 5 \times 5 \times 5 \times 5$ | 15,625 |
| $7^4$ | 7 to the fourth power | $7 \times 7 \times 7 \times 7$ | 2,401 |
| $9^3$ | 9 to the third power or 9 cubed | $9 \times 9 \times 9$ | 729 |

**Example 1**   Write $6 \times 6 \times 6$ using an exponent. Then find the value.

The base is 6. Since 6 is a factor 3 times, the exponent is 3.
$6 \times 6 \times 6 = 6^3$ or 216

**Example 2**   Write $2^4$ as a product of the same factor. Then find the value.

The base is 2. The exponent is 4. So, 2 is a factor 4 times.
$2^4 = 2 \times 2 \times 2 \times 2$ or 16

**Example 3**   Write the prime factorization of 225 using exponents.

The prime factorization of 225 can be written as $3 \times 3 \times 5 \times 5$, or $3^2 \times 5^2$.

### Exercises

Write each product using an exponent. Then find the value.

1. $2 \times 2 \times 2 \times 2 \times 2$

2. $9 \times 9$

3. $3 \times 3 \times 3$

4. $5 \times 5 \times 5$

5. $3 \times 3 \times 3 \times 3 \times 3$

6. $10 \times 10$

Write each power as a product of the same factor. Then find the value.

7. $7^2$

8. $4^3$

9. $8^4$

10. $5^5$

11. $2^8$

12. $7^3$

Write the prime factorization of each number using exponents.

13. 40

14. 75

15. 100

16. 147

**22**

## 1-3 Skills Practice

### Powers and Exponents

**Write each expression in words.**

1. $7^2$

2. $8^3$

3. $4^4$

4. $5^6$

**Write each product using an exponent. Then find the value.**

5. $4 \times 4 \times 4 \times 4$           6. $3 \times 3 \times 3 \times 3$

7. $5 \times 5 \times 5 \times 5$           8. $7 \times 7$

9. $3 \times 3 \times 3 \times 3 \times 3$           10. $2 \times 2 \times 2 \times 2 \times 2 \times 2$

11. $6 \times 6 \times 6$           12. $6 \times 6 \times 6 \times 6$

**Write each power as a product of the same factor. Then find the value.**

13. $3^8$           14. $2^5$

15. $8^3$           16. $10^5$

17. $6^2$           18. $7^4$

19. $2^3$           20. $3^5$

21. $6^5$           22. $2^7$

**Write the prime factorization of each number using exponents.**

23. 54           24. 36

25. 63           26. 245

Lesson 1-3

## 1-3 Practice

### Powers and Exponents

**Write each product using an exponent.**

1. $6 \times 6$

2. $10 \times 10 \times 10 \times 10$

3. $4 \times 4 \times 4 \times 4 \times 4$

4. $8 \times 8 \times 8 \times 8 \times 8 \times 8 \times 8 \times 8$

5. $5 \times 5 \times 5 \times 5 \times 5 \times 5$

6. $13 \times 13 \times 13$

**Write each power as a product of the same factor. Then find the value.**

7. $10^1$

8. $2^7$

9. $8^3$

10. $3^8$

11. nine squared

12. four to the sixth power

**Write the prime factorization of each number using exponents.**

13. 32

14. 100

15. 63

16. 99

17. 52

18. 147

19. **LABELS** A sheet of labels has 8 rows of labels with 8 labels in each row. How many total labels are on the sheet? Write your answer using exponents, and then find the value.

20. **CANDLES** To find how much wax the candle mold holds, use the expression $s \times s \times s$, where $s$ is the length of a side. Write this expression as a power. The amount of wax the mold holds is measured in cubic units. How many cubic units of wax does the mold hold?

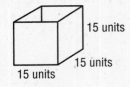

15 units
15 units
15 units

## 1-3 Word Problem Practice

### Powers and Exponents

---

**1. SPACE** The Sun is about $10 \cdot 10$ million miles away from Earth. Write $10 \cdot 10$ using an exponent. Then find the value of the power. How many miles away is the Sun?

**2. WEIGHT** A 100-pound person on Earth would weigh about $4 \cdot 4 \cdot 4 \cdot 4$ pounds on Jupiter. Write $4 \cdot 4 \cdot 4 \cdot 4$ using an exponent. Then find the value of the power. How much would a 100-pound person weigh on Jupiter?

---

**3. ELECTIONS** In the year 2000, the governor of Washington, Gary Locke, received about $10^6$ votes to win the election. Write this as a product. How many votes did Gary Locke receive?

**4. SPACE** The diameter of Mars is about $9^4$ kilometers. Write $9^4$ as a product. Then find the value of the product.

---

**5. SPACE** The length of one day on Venus is $3^5$ Earth days. Express this exponent as a product. Then find the value of the product:

**6. GEOGRAPHY** The area of San Bernardino County, California, the largest county in the U.S., is about $3^9$ square miles. Write this as a product. What is the area of San Bernardino County?

---

**7. GEOMETRY** The volume of the block shown can be found by multiplying the width, length, and height. Write the volume using an exponent. Find the volume.

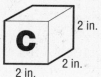

**8. SPACE** A day on Jupiter lasts about 10 hours. Write a product and an exponent to show how many hours are in 10 Jupiter days. Then find the value of the power.

---

Lesson 1-3

## 1-3 Enrichment

## The Sieve of Erathosthenes

Erathosthenes was a Greek mathematician who lived from about 276 B.C. to 194 B.C. He devised the **Sieve of Erathosthenes** as a method of identifying all the prime numbers up to a certain number. Using the chart below, you can use his method to find all the prime numbers up to 120. Just follow these numbered steps.

1. The number 1 is not prime. Cross it out.

2. The number 2 is prime. Circle it. Then cross out every second number—4, 6, 8, 10, and so on.

3. The number 3 is prime. Circle it. Then cross out every third number—6, 9, 12, and so on.

4. The number 4 is crossed out. Go to the next number that is not crossed out.

5. The number 5 is prime. Circle it. Then cross out every fifth number—10, 15, 20, 25, and so on.

6. Continue crossing out numbers as described in Steps 2–5. The numbers that remain at the end of this process are prime numbers.

7. **CHALLENGE** Look at the prime numbers that are circled in the chart. Do you see a pattern among the prime numbers that are greater than 3? What do you think the pattern is?

| 1 | 2 | 3 | 4 | 5 | 6 |
|---|---|---|---|---|---|
| 7 | 8 | 9 | 10 | 11 | 12 |
| 13 | 14 | 15 | 16 | 17 | 18 |
| 19 | 20 | 21 | 22 | 23 | 24 |
| 25 | 26 | 27 | 28 | 29 | 30 |
| 31 | 32 | 33 | 34 | 35 | 36 |
| 37 | 38 | 39 | 40 | 41 | 42 |
| 43 | 44 | 45 | 46 | 47 | 48 |
| 49 | 50 | 51 | 52 | 53 | 54 |
| 55 | 56 | 57 | 58 | 59 | 60 |
| 61 | 62 | 63 | 64 | 65 | 66 |
| 67 | 68 | 69 | 70 | 71 | 72 |
| 73 | 74 | 75 | 76 | 77 | 78 |
| 79 | 80 | 81 | 82 | 83 | 84 |
| 85 | 86 | 87 | 88 | 89 | 90 |
| 91 | 92 | 93 | 94 | 95 | 96 |
| 97 | 98 | 99 | 100 | 101 | 102 |
| 103 | 104 | 105 | 106 | 107 | 108 |
| 109 | 110 | 111 | 112 | 113 | 114 |
| 115 | 116 | 117 | 118 | 119 | 120 |

# 1-3 TI-83/84 Plus Activity

## Exponents

You can use a graphing calculator to evaluate expressions involving exponents.

**Example 1**  Evaluate $5^4 + 6^2$.

Enter: 5 [^] 4 [+] 6 [x²] [ENTER]  661

So, $5^4 + 6^2 = 661$.

You can also use a graphing calculator to evaluate algebraic expressions that involve exponents. You store the variables' values in the memory before evaluating all of the expressions.

**Example 2**  Evaluate $x^3 + y^4$ if $x = 2$ and $y = 5$.

Enter: 2 [STO▸] [ALPHA] X [ENTER] 5 [STO▸] [ALPHA] Y [ENTER] [ALPHA] X [^]

   3 [+] [ALPHA] Y [^] 4 [ENTER]  633

So, $x^3 + y^4 = 633$ when $x = 2$ and $y = 5$.

**Exercises**

Evaluate each expression.

1. $6 + 3^4 + 1$

2. $4^5 + 10^7$

3. $7^3 - 1^9 - 2^6$

4. $4 + 3^5 - 5 - 2$

5. $27 - 5^2 + 7^2$

6. $6^6 - 5^5 + 4^4$

7. $9^4 + 16 \div 2^2 - 24 \div 3$

8. $10^1 - 9^2 + 8^3 - 7^4 + 6^5$

Evaluate each expression if $x = 6$ and $y = 3$.

9. $x^4$

10. $y^5 + 2$

11. $x^3 + 5^3$

12. $x^3 + y^8$

13. $3x^2 + y^4$

14. $x^5 \cdot 2y^4 - 126$

15. $xy^8$

16. $5y^5 + 5x^5$

17. $x^{10} - 10xy$

18. $4xy + 2y^3 + xy - x^4 + y^{10}$

19. $xy^5 + 5y + yx^5 + 5x$

**Lesson 1-3**

## 1-4  Lesson Reading Guide

### Order of Operations

## Get Ready for the Lesson

**Read the introduction at the top of page 37 in your textbook.**
**Write your answers below.**

1. How much would 3 boxes of popcorn cost? 4 sandwiches?

2. Find the total cost of buying 3 boxes of popcorn and 4 sandwiches.

3. What two operations did you use in Questions 1 and 2? Explain how to find the answer to Question 2 using these operations.

## Read the Lesson

4. The steps for finding the value of a numerical expression are listed below. Number the steps in the correct order.

   _____ Find the value of all powers.
   _____ Add and subtract in order from left to right.
   _____ Simplify the expressions inside grouping symbols.
   _____ Multiply and divide in order from left to right.

5. Using the order of operations, explain how you would find the value of $(7 + 5) \div 2^2 + 8$.

6. How would the value of $(7 + 5) \div 2^2 + 8$ differ if you added the 8 before you divided by 4?

## Remember What You Learned

7. Using only operation symbols and grouping symbols, write the order of operations.

## 1-4 Study Guide and Intervention

### Order of Operations

**Order of Operations**
1. Simplify the expressions inside grouping symbols, like parentheses.
2. Find the value of all powers.
3. Multiply and divide in order from left to right.
4. Add and subtract in order from left to right.

**Example 1** **Find the value of $48 \div (3 + 3) - 2^2$.**

$$48 \div (3 + 3) - 2^2 = 48 \div 6 - 2^2 \qquad \text{Simplify the expression inside the parentheses.}$$
$$= 48 \div 6 - 4 \qquad \text{Find } 2^2.$$
$$= 8 - 4 \qquad \text{Divide 48 by 6.}$$
$$= 4 \qquad \text{Subtract 4 from 8.}$$

**Example 2** **Write and solve an expression to find the total cost of planting flowers in the garden.**

| Item | Cost Per Item | Number of Items Needed |
|------|---------------|------------------------|
| pack of flowers | $4 | 5 |
| bag of dirt | $3 | 1 |
| bottle of fertilizer | $4 | 1 |

| Words | cost of 5 flower packs | plus | cost of dirt | plus | cost of fertilizer |
|-------|------------------------|------|--------------|------|--------------------|
| Expression | $5 \times \$4$ | + | $3 | + | $4 |

$$5 \times \$4 + \$3 + \$4 = \$20 + \$3 + \$4$$
$$= \$23 + \$4$$
$$= \$27$$

The total cost of planting flowers in the garden is $27.

### Exercises

**Find the value of each expression.**

**1.** $7 + 2 \times 3$

**2.** $12 \div 3 + 5$

**3.** $16 - (4 + 5)$

**4.** $8 \times 8 \div 4$

**5.** $10 + 14 \div 2$

**6.** $3 \times 3 + 2 \times 4$

**7.** $80 - 8 \times 3^2$

**8.** $11 \times (9 - 2^2)$

**9.** $25 \div 5 + 6 \times (12 - 4)$

**10. GARDENING** Refer to Example 2 above. Suppose that the gardener did not buy enough flowers and goes back to the store to purchase four more packs. She also purchases a hoe for $16. Write an expression that shows the total amount she spent to plant flowers in her garden.

**Lesson 1-4**

## 1-4 Skills Practice

### *Order of Operations*

**Find the value of each expression.**

**1.** $7 - 6 + 5$

**2.** $31 + 19 - 8$

**3.** $64 - 8 + 21$

**4.** $17 + 34 - 2$

**5.** $28 + (89 - 67)$

**6.** $(8 + 1) \times 12 - 13$

**7.** $63 \div 9 + 8$

**8.** $5 \times 6 - (9 - 4)$

**9.** $13 \times 4 - 72 \div 8$

**10.** $16 \div 2 + 8 \times 3$

**11.** $30 \div (21 - 6) \times 4$

**12.** $6 \times 7 \div (6 + 8)$

**13.** $88 - 16 \times 5 + 2 - 3$

**14.** $(2 + 6) \div 2 + 4 \times 3$

**15.** $4^3 - 24 \div 8$

**16.** $100 \div 5^2 \times 4^3$

**17.** $48 \div 2^3 + 25 \times (9 - 7)$

**18.** $45 \div 9 + 8 - 7 + 2 \times 3$

**19.** $18 + 7^2 \times (8 - 2) \div 3 + 8$

**20.** $(5^2 + 3^3) \times (81 + 9) \div 10$

## 1-4 Practice

### *Order of Operations*

**Find the value of each expression.**

**1.** $34 + 17 - 5$

**2.** $25 - 14 + 3$

**3.** $42 + 6 \div 2$

**4.** $39 \times (15 \div 3) - 16$

**5.** $48 \div 8 + 5 \times (7 - 2)$

**6.** $64 \div (15 - 7) \times 2 - 9$

**7.** $(3 + 7) \times 6 + 4$

**8.** $9 + 8 \times 3 - (5 \times 2)$

**9.** $7^2 + 6 \times 2$

**10.** $34 - 8^2 \div 4$

**11.** $45 \div 3 \times 2^3$

**12.** $4 \times (5^2 - 12) - 6$

**13.** $78 - 2^4 \div (14 - 6) \times 2$

**14.** $9 + 7 \times (15 + 3) \div 3^2$

**15.** $13 + (4^3 \div 2) \times 5 - 17$

**16.** Using symbols, write the product of 18 and 7 plus 5.

**ART For Exercises 17 and 18, use the following information.**

An art supply store sells posters for $9 each and picture frames for $15 each.

**17.** Write an expression for the total cost of 6 posters and 6 frames.

**18.** What is the total cost for 6 framed posters?

**19. SCIENCE** There are 24 students in a science class. Mr. Sato will give each pair of students 3 magnets. So far, Mr. Sato has given 9 pairs of students their 3 magnets. How many more magnets does Mr. Sato need so that each pair of students has exactly 3 magnets?

Lesson 1-4

## 1-4 Word Problem Practice

### Order of Operations

**MONEY** For Exercises 1–3, use the table that shows the price of admission to a movie theater.

| Movie Theater Admission |
|---|
| Adults: $8 |
| Children (under 13): $5 |
| Matinee (before 6 P.M.): $3 |

1. Janelle (age 12) and her cousin, Marquita (age 14), go to a 7:00 P.M. show. Write an expression for the total cost of admission. What is the total cost?

2. Jan takes her three children and two neighbor's children to a matinee. All of the children are under age 13. Write an expression for the total cost of admission. How much in all did Jan pay for admission?

3. Connor (age 13), his sister (age 7), and Connor's parents go to a movie on Saturday night. Write an expression for the total cost. What is the total cost?

4. **SOCCER** Eduardo is 16. Eduardo's dad takes him and his younger sister to a soccer match. Tickets are $17 for adults and $13 for children (18 and under). Write an expression for the total cost of the tickets. What is the total cost of the tickets?

5. **MONEY** Frankie orders two hamburgers and a soda for lunch. A hamburger is $3 and a soda is $1.00. Write an expression to show how much he paid for lunch. Then find the value of the expression.

6. **MONEY** A store sells barrettes for $2 each and combs for $1. Shelby buys 3 barrettes and a comb. Kendra buys 2 barrettes and 4 combs. Write an expression for the amount the two girls spent all together. Find the total amount spent.

## 1-4 Enrichment

## Operations Puzzles

Now that you have learned how to evaluate an expression using the order of operations, can you work backward? In this activity, the value of the expression will be given to you. It is your job to decide what the operations or the numbers must be in order to arrive at that value.

**Fill in each** ☐ **with +, −, ×, or ÷ to make a true statement.**

**1.** 48 ☐ 3 ☐ 12 = 12

**2.** 30 ☐ 15 ☐ 3 = 6

**3.** 24 ☐ 12 ☐ 6 ☐ 3 = 4

**4.** 24 ☐ 12 ☐ 6 ☐ 3 = 18

**5.** 4 ☐ 16 ☐ 2 ☐ 8 = 24

**6.** 45 ☐ 3 ☐ 3 ☐ 9 = 3

**7.** 36 ☐ 2 ☐ 3 ☐ 12 ☐ 2 = 0

**8.** 72 ☐ 12 ☐ 4 ☐ 8 ☐ 3 = 0

**Fill in each** ☐ **with one of the given numbers to make a true statement. Each number may be used only once.**

**9.** 6, 12, 24

☐ ÷ ☐ × ☐ = 12

**10.** 4, 9, 36

☐ − ☐ ÷ ☐ = 0

**11.** 6, 8, 12, 24

☐ ÷ ☐ + ☐ − ☐ = 4

**12.** 2, 5, 10, 50

☐ − ☐ ÷ ☐ + ☐ = 50

**13.** 2, 4, 6, 8, 10

☐ ÷ ☐ × ☐ + ☐ − ☐ = 0

**14.** 1, 3, 5, 7, 9

☐ ÷ ☐ + ☐ − ☐ ÷ ☐ = 1

**15. CHALLENGE** Fill in each ☐ with one of the digits from 1 through 9 to make a true statement. Each digit may be used only once.

☐ ÷ ☐ × ☐ + ☐ × ☐ × ☐ ÷ ☐ + ☐ × ☐ = 100

**Lesson 1-4**

# 1-4  Scientific Calculator Activity

## Order of Operations

Scientific calculators follow the correct order of operations.

**Example 1**    Evaluate $18 + 3 \times 2$.

**Enter:**   18 [+] 3 [×] 2 [ENTER =]

If the display is 24, then the calculator follows the correct order of operations. If the display is 42, use parentheses to show the operation to be performed first as in the following example.

**Example 2**    Evaluate $18 + (3 \times 2)$.

**Enter:**   18 [+] [(] 3 [×] 2 [)] [ENTER =] 24

The correct answer is 24.

**Exercises**

Use a calculator to find the value of each expression.
Use parentheses if necessary.

1. $112 - 4 \times 23$

2. $15 + 12 \div 2$

3. $14 + 28 \div 7$

4. $25 + 10 - 5 \div 5$

5. $200 - 10 \times 10 \times 2$

6. $12 \div 4 \times 2 + 8$

7. $20 \div 2 \times 10$

8. $114 + 10 - 9 \times 9$

9. $28 + 42 \div 7 \div 2$

10. $125 - 100 - 25 \div 5$

**CHALLENGE**

11. $24 \div 4 \times 2 + 8 \div 4 + 4$

12. $75 + 5 \times 5 \div 10 \times 10$

## 1-5  Lesson Reading Guide

### *Algebra: Variables and Expressions*

## Get Ready for the Lesson

**Read the introduction at the top of page 42 in your textbook.
Write your answers below.**

1. What does *some number* represent?

2. Find the value of the expression *the sum of two and some number* if *some number* is 14.

3. Assume you have two boxes of crayons each with the same number of crayons inside. Write an expression that represents the total number of pieces of crayons in both boxes.

## Read the Lesson

4. Look up the word *variable* in a dictionary. What definition of the word matches its use in this lesson? If classmates use different dictionaries, compare the meanings among the dictionaries.

5. The introduction uses the expression *some number*, which can also be read as "some unknown value." In the expression *some unknown value*, would the expression *value of the variable* mean the same thing?

## Remember What You Learned

6. Explain the difference between a numerical expression and an algebraic expression.

Lesson 1-5

# 1-5 Study Guide and Intervention

## Algebra: Variables and Expressions

- A **variable** is a symbol, usually a letter, used to represent a number.
- Multiplication in algebra can be shown as $4n$, $4 \cdot n$, or $4 \times n$.
- **Algebraic expressions** are combinations of variables, numbers, and at least one operation.

**Example 1** Evaluate $35 + x$ if $x = 6$.

$$35 + x = 35 + 6 \qquad \text{Replace } x \text{ with 6.}$$
$$\phantom{35 + x} = 41 \qquad \text{Add 35 and 6.}$$

**Example 2** Evaluate $y + x$ if $x = 21$ and $y = 35$.

$$y + x = 35 + 21 \qquad \text{Replace } x \text{ with 21 and } y \text{ with 35.}$$
$$\phantom{y + x} = 56 \qquad \text{Add 35 and 21.}$$

**Example 3** Evaluate $4n + 3$ if $n = 2$.

$$4n + 3 = 4 \times 2 + 3 \qquad \text{Replace } n \text{ with 2.}$$
$$\phantom{4n + 3} = 8 + 3 \qquad \text{Find the product of 4 and 2.}$$
$$\phantom{4n + 3} = 11 \qquad \text{Add 8 and 3.}$$

**Example 4** Evaluate $4n - 2$ if $n = 5$.

$$4n - 2 = 4 \times 5 - 2 \qquad \text{Replace } n \text{ with 5.}$$
$$\phantom{4n - 2} = 20 - 2 \qquad \text{Find the product of 4 and 5.}$$
$$\phantom{4n - 2} = 18 \qquad \text{Subtract 2 from 20.}$$

### Exercises

Evaluate each expression if $y = 4$.

1. $3 + y$
2. $y + 8$
3. $4 \times y$

4. $9y$
5. $15y$
6. $300y$

7. $y^2$
8. $y^2 + 18$
9. $y^2 + 3 \times 7$

Evaluate each expression if $m = 3$ and $k = 10$.

10. $16 + m$
11. $4k$
12. $m \times k$

13. $m + k$
14. $7m + k$
15. $6k + m$

16. $3k - 4m$
17. $2mk$
18. $5k - 6m$

19. $20m \div k$
20. $m^3 + 2k^2$
21. $k^2 \div (2 + m)$

# 1-5 Skills Practice

## Algebra: Variables and Expressions

**Complete the table.**

| Algebraic Expressions | Variables | Numbers | Operations |
|---|---|---|---|
| **1.** $5d + 2c$ | ? | ? | ? |
| **2.** $5w - 4y + 2s$ | ? | ? | ? |
| **3.** $xy \div 4 + 3m - 6$ | ? | ? | ? |

**Evaluate each expression if $a = 3$ and $b = 4$.**

**4.** $10 + b$

**5.** $2a + 8$

**6.** $4b - 5a$

**7.** $a \times b$

**8.** $7a \times 9b$

**9.** $8a - 9$

**10.** $b \times 22$

**11.** $a^2 + 1$

**12.** $18 \div 2a$

**13.** $a^2 \times b^2$

**14.** $ab \div 3$

**15.** $15a - 4b$

**16.** $ab + 7 \times 11$

**17.** $36 \div 6a$

**18.** $7a + 8b \times 2$

**Evaluate each expression if $x = 7$, $y = 15$, and $z = 8$.**

**19.** $x + y + z$

**20.** $x + 2z$

**21.** $xz + 3y$

**22.** $4x - 3z$

**23.** $z^2 \div 4$

**24.** $6z - 5z$

**25.** $9y \div (2x + 1)$

**26.** $15y + x^2$

**27.** $y^2 + 4 \times 6$

**28.** $y^2 - 2x^2$

**29.** $x^2 + 30 - 18$

**30.** $13y - zx \div 4$

**31.** $xz - 2y + 8$

**32.** $z^2 + 5y - 20$

**33.** $3y \times 40x - 1,000$

Lesson 1-5

# 1-5 Practice

## *Algebra: Variables and Expressions*

**Evaluate each expression if $m = 6$ and $n = 12$.**

**1.** $m + 5$      **2.** $n - 7$      **3.** $m \cdot 4$      **4.** $m + n$

**5.** $n - m$      **6.** $12 \div n$      **7.** $9 \cdot n$      **8.** $n \div m$

**9.** $2m + 5$      **10.** $4m - 17$      **11.** $36 - 6m$      **12.** $3n + 8$

**Evaluate each expression if $a = 9$, $b = 3$, and $c = 12$.**

**13.** $4a - 17$      **14.** $14 + 2c$      **15.** $c \div 2$

**16.** $ac$      **17.** $c \div b$      **18.** $2ac$

**19.** $b^3 + c$      **20.** $19 + 6a \div 2$      **21.** $4b^2 \cdot 3$

**22.** $3c \div (2b^2)$      **23.** $c^2 - (3a)$      **24.** $ac \div (2b)$

**25. ANIMALS** A Gentoo penguin can swim at a rate of 17 miles per hour. How many miles can a penguin swim in 4 hours? Use the expression $rt$, where $r$ represents rate and $t$ represents time.

**26. CLOTHING** A company charges $6 to make a pattern for an order of T-shirts and $11 for each T-shirt it produces from the pattern. The expression $11n + $6 represents the cost of $n$ T-shirts with the same pattern. Find the total cost for 5 T-shirts with the same pattern.

## 1-5 Word Problem Practice

### Algebra: Variables and Expressions

**TRAVEL** For Exercises 1 and 2, use the table that shows the distance between cities in Arizona.

### Arizona Mileage Chart

|  | Flagstaff | Phoenix | Tucson | Nogales |
|---|---|---|---|---|
| **Phoenix** | 136 miles |  | 117 miles | 181 miles |
| **Tucson** | 253 miles | 117 miles |  | 64 miles |
| **Nogales** | 317 miles | 181 miles | 64 miles |  |

1. To find the speed of a car, use the expression $d \div t$ where $d$ represents the distance and $t$ represents time. Find the speed of a car that travels from Phoenix to Flagstaff in 2 hours.

2. To find the time it will take for a bicyclist to travel from Nogales to Tucson, use the expression $\frac{d}{s}$ where $d$ represents distance and $s$ represents speed. Find the time if the bicyclist travels at a speed of 16 miles per hour.

3. **PERIMETER** The perimeter of a rectangle can be found using the formula $2\ell + 2w$, where $\ell$ represents the length and $w$ represents the width. Find the perimeter if $\ell = 6$ units and $w = 3$ units.

$\ell$

$w$

4. **PERIMETER** Another formula for perimeter is $2(\ell + w)$. Find the perimeter of the rectangle in Exercise 3 using this formula. How do the answers compare? Explain how you used order of operations using this formula.

5. **SHOPPING** Write an expression using a variable that shows how much 3 pairs of jeans will cost if you do not know the price of the jeans. Assume each pair costs the same amount.

6. **SHOPPING** Write an expression using variables to show how much 3 plain T-shirts and 2 printed T-shirts will cost, assuming that the prices of plain and printed T-shirts are not the same.

Lesson 1-5

## 1-5  Enrichment

## Using Formulas

A formula is an equation that can be used to solve certain kinds of problems.
Formulas often have algebraic expressions. Here are some common formulas
used to solve geometry problems. The variables in geometric formulas
represent dimensions of the geometric figures.

Area ($A$)
  of a rectangle: $A = \ell \times w$
  of a square: $A = s^2$
  of a triangle: $A = \frac{1}{2}bh$
  of a square: $P = 4s$

Volume ($V$)
  of a rectangular prism: $V = \ell \times w \times h$

Perimeter ($P$)
  of a rectangle: $P = 2(w + \ell)$

$b$ = base   $h$ = height   $\ell$ = length   $s$ = side   $w$ = width

**Write the formula that would be used to solve each problem.**

1. Jack wants to put a fence around his garden to keep rabbits out. Jack's
garden is square shape. Which formula can Jack use to find how much
fence he needs to buy?

2. Diane's mother will replace the carpeting in their living room. The living
room is rectangular in shape. Which formula can Diane's mother use to
determine how much carpeting she will need to order for her living room?

3. Victor is cleaning his aquarium, which is shaped like a rectangular prism.
After he empties the aquarium and cleans the sides, he will refill the
aquarium. Which formula can Victor use to determine how much water he
will put back in the aquarium?

4. Joann is making a triangular flag for a school project. Which formula can
she use to determine how much material she needs to buy to make the flag?

**Solve each problem.**

5. A tablecloth is 8 feet long and 5 feet wide. What is the area of the
tablecloth?

6. Jessica wants to frame a square picture that has sides of 6 inches. How
many inches of wood will she need to make the frame?

7. How many cubic centimeters of packing peanuts will fit in a cardboard box
that is 9 centimeters long, 8 centimeters wide, and 3 centimeters high?

8. Joaquin is painting a mural on one wall of the school's gymnasium. Part of
the mural is a triangle with a base of 20 ft and a height of 8 feet. What is
the area of the triangle?

## 1-6 Lesson Reading Guide

### Algebra: Functions

## Get Ready for the Lesson

**Read the introduction at the top of page 49 in your textbook. Write your answers below.**

1. Write an expression to represent the number of times a hummingbird beats its wings in 2 seconds; in 6 seconds; and in $s$ seconds.

## Read the Lesson

2. If you look up the word *function* in a dictionary, you might find a definition like the following: a quantity whose value depends on that of another quantity or quantities. In the function $600t$, what does the value of $600t$ depend on?

3. Find the function rule for the table below. _____

| Input ($x$) | Output (■) |
|:---:|:---:|
| 0 | 3 |
| 2 | 5 |
| 4 | 7 |

## Remember What You Learned

4. Work with a partner. Each of you should create a table like the one in Exercise 3 above. Decide on a function rule to use for the output quantities, but do not write the rule. Exchange tables with your partner. Identify the function rule that expresses the relationship between the input quantity and the output quantity.

## 1-6 Study Guide and Intervention

### Algebra: Functions

A **function rule** describes the relationship between the input and output of a **function**. The inputs and outputs can be organized in a **function table**.

**Example 1** Complete the function table.

| Input ($x$) | Output ($x - 3$) |
|---|---|
| 9 | ■ |
| 8 | ■ |
| 6 | ■ |

The function rule is $n - 7$. Subtract 7 from each input.

| Input | | Output |
|---|---|---|
| 9 | $- 3 \rightarrow$ | 6 |
| 8 | $- 3 \rightarrow$ | 5 |
| 6 | $- 3 \rightarrow$ | 3 |

$\rightarrow$

| Input ($x$) | Output ($x - 3$) |
|---|---|
| 9 | 6 |
| 8 | 5 |
| 6 | 3 |

**Example 2** Find the rule for the function table.

| Input ($x$) | Output (■) |
|---|---|
| 0 | 0 |
| 1 | 4 |
| 2 | 8 |

Study the relationship between each input and output.

| Input | | Output |
|---|---|---|
| 0 | $\times 4 \rightarrow$ | 0 |
| 1 | $\times 4 \rightarrow$ | 4 |
| 2 | $\times 4 \rightarrow$ | 8 |

The output is four times the input. So, the function rule is $4x$.

### Exercises

Complete each function table.

1.
| Input ($x$) | Output ($2x$) |
|---|---|
| 0 | |
| 2 | |
| 4 | |

2.
| Input ($x$) | Output ($4 + x$) |
|---|---|
| 0 | |
| 1 | |
| 4 | |

Find the rule for each function table.

3.
| Input ($x$) | Output (■) |
|---|---|
| 1 | 3 |
| 2 | 4 |
| 5 | 7 |

4.
| Input ($x$) | Output (■) |
|---|---|
| 2 | 1 |
| 6 | 3 |
| 10 | 5 |

## 1-6  Skills Practice

### Algebra: Functions

Lesson 1-6

Complete each function table.

**1.**

| Input (x) | Output (x + 3) |
|-----------|----------------|
| 0 | |
| 2 | |
| 4 | |

**2.**

| Input (x) | Output (3x) |
|-----------|-------------|
| 0 | |
| 1 | |
| 2 | |

**3.**

| Input (x) | Output (x − 1) |
|-----------|----------------|
| 7 | |
| 5 | |
| 4 | |

**4.**

| Input (x) | Output (x ÷ 3) |
|-----------|----------------|
| 12 | |
| 9 | |
| 6 | |

**5.** If a function rule is $2x - 3$, what is the output for 3?

**6.** If a function rule is $4 - x$, what is the output for 2?

**Find the rule for each function table. Write the rule in the table.**

**7.**

| x | |
|----|----|
| 10 | 7 |
| 7 | 4 |
| 4 | 1 |

**8.**

| x | |
|----|----|
| 3 | 12 |
| 6 | 15 |
| 8 | 17 |

**9.**

| x | |
|----|----|
| 0 | 0 |
| 2 | 10 |
| 3 | 15 |

**10.**

| x | |
|----|----|
| 4 | 2 |
| 6 | 3 |
| 12 | 6 |

## 1-6 Practice

### Algebra: Functions

**Complete each function table.**

1.

| Input ($x$) | Output ($x + 6$) |
|---|---|
| 0 | |
| 3 | |
| 7 | |

2.

| Input ($x$) | Output ($x - 1$) |
|---|---|
| 1 | |
| 4 | |
| 8 | |

3.

| Input ($x$) | Output ($3x$) |
|---|---|
| 0 | |
| 2 | |
| 4 | |

4.

| Input ($x$) | Output ($x \div 2$) |
|---|---|
| 4 | |
| 8 | |
| 10 | |

**Find the rule for each function table.**

5.

| $x$ | ■ |
|---|---|
| 4 | 1 |
| 8 | 2 |
| 16 | 4 |

6.

| $x$ | ■ |
|---|---|
| 12 | 8 |
| 13 | 9 |
| 15 | 11 |

7.

| $x$ | ■ |
|---|---|
| 2 | 1 |
| 6 | 3 |
| 10 | 5 |

8.

| $x$ | ■ |
|---|---|
| 3 | 0 |
| 5 | 2 |
| 6 | 3 |
| 8 | 5 |
| 11 | 8 |

9.

| $x$ | ■ |
|---|---|
| 0 | 3 |
| 1 | 6 |
| 2 | 9 |
| 3 | 12 |
| 4 | 15 |

10.

| $x$ | ■ |
|---|---|
| 2 | 5 |
| 4 | 13 |
| 6 | 21 |
| 8 | 29 |
| 10 | 37 |

11. **FOOD** A pizza place sells pizzas for $7 each plus a $4 delivery charge per order. If Pat orders 3 pizzas to be delivered, what will be his total cost?

12. **MOVIES** A store sells used DVDs for $8 each and used videotapes for $6 each. Write a function rule to represent the total selling price of DVDs ($d$) and videotapes ($v$). Then use the function rule to find the price of 5 DVDs and 3 videotapes.

# 1-6 Word Problem Practice

## Algebra: Functions

Lesson 1-6

**1. DRAGONS** The Luck Dragons that live in the Enchanted Forest weigh $4x$ pounds when they are $x$ years old. Write a function table that can be used to find the weights of 6-year old, 8-year old, and 10-year old Luck Dragons.

**2. ROLLER COASTER** Twelve people are able to ride the Serpent of Fire roller coaster at one time. Write a function table that shows the total number of people that have been on the roller coaster after 1, 2, 3, and 4 rides.

**3. MOVIES** At the local movie theater it costs $10.00 for 2 students to see a movie. It costs $15.00 for 3 students, and it costs $20.00 for 4 students. Let the number of students be the input. What is the function rule that relates the number of students to the cost of tickets?

**4. HOMEWORK** At Elmwood Middle School, sixth graders spend 1 hour every night doing homework. Seventh graders spend 2 hours, and eighth graders spend 3 hours. Let the students' grade be the input. What is the function rule between the students' grade and the amount of time the students spend on homework every night?

**5. BEADS** A bead shop sells wooden beads for $3 each and glass beads for $7 each. Write a function rule to represent the total selling price of wooden ($w$) and glass ($g$) beads.

**6.** Use the function rule in Exercise 5 to find the selling price of 20 wooden beads and 4 glass beads.

## 1-6  Enrichment

## Function Rules and Dot Patterns

Function rules are often used to describe geometric patterns. In the pattern at the right, for example, do you see this relationship?

1st figure:  $3 \times 1 = 3$ dots
2nd figure:  $3 \times 2 = 6$ dots
3rd figure:  $3 \times 3 = 9$ dots
4th figure:  $3 \times 4 = 12$ dots

So the "nth" figure in this pattern would have $3 \times n$, or $3n$, dots. A function rule that describes the pattern is $3n$.

1st  →  3 dots

2nd  →  6 dots

3rd  →  9 dots

4th  →  12 dots

**Write a function rule to describe each dot pattern.**

**1.** 1st 2nd 3rd 4th

**2.** 1st 2nd 3rd 4th

**3.** 1st 2nd 3rd 4th

**4.** 1st 2nd 3rd 4th

**5.** 1st 2nd 3rd 4th

**6.** 1st 2nd 3rd 4th

**7. CHALLENGE** Create your own dot pattern. Then exchange patterns with a classmate. Try to find the function rule for each other's patterns.

# 1-7 Study Guide and Intervention

## Problem-Solving Investigation: Guess and Check

Lesson 1-7

When solving problems, one strategy that is helpful to use is *guess and check*. Based on the information in the problem, you can make a guess of the solution. Then use computations to check if your guess is correct. You can repeat this process until you find the correct solution.

You can use guess and check, along with the following four-step problem solving plan to solve a problem.

**1 Understand** – Read and get a general understanding of the problem.

**2 Plan** – Make a plan to solve the problem and estimate the solution.

**3 Solve** – Use your plan to solve the problem.

**4 Check** – Check the reasonableness of your solution.

**Example 1** SPORTS Meagan made a combination of 2-point baskets and 3-point baskets in the basketball game. She scored a total of 9 points. How many 2-point baskets and 3-point baskets did Meagan make in the basketball game?

**Understand** You know that she made both 2-point and 3-point baskets. You also know she scored a total of 9 points. You need to find how many of each she made.

**Plan** Make a guess until you find an answer that makes sense for the problem.

**Solve**

| Number of 2-point baskets | Number of 3-point baskets | Total Number of Points |
|---|---|---|
| 1 | 2 | $1(2) + 2(3) = 8$ |
| 2 | 2 | $2(2) + 2(3) = 10$ |
| 2 | 1 | $2(2) + 1(3) = 7$ |
| 3 | 1 | $3(2) + 1(3) = 9$ |

**Check** Three 2-point baskets result in 6 points. One 3-point basket results in 3 points. Since $6 + 3$ is 9, the answer is correct.

**Exercise**

VIDEO GAMES Juan has 16 video games. The types of video games he has are sports games, treasure hunts, and puzzles. He has 4 more sports games than treasure hunts. He has 3 fewer puzzles than treasure hunts. Use guess and check to determine how many of each type of video game Juan has.

## 1-7 Skills Practice

### Problem-Solving Investigation: Guess and Check

**Use the guess and check strategy to solve each problem.**

1. **MONEY** Keegan has 10 coins in his pocket that total $2.05. He only has quarters and dimes. How many of each coin does Keegan have?

2. **NUMBERS** Ms. Junkin told her students that she was thinking of three numbers between 1 and 9 that had a sum of 19. Find the three possible numbers.

3. **SHOPPING** Natasha bought some bracelets and some rings during a jewelry store sale. Each bracelet cost $4 and each ring cost $7. If Natasha spent $29 on the jewelry, how many bracelets and rings did she buy?

4. **ORDER OF OPERATIONS** Use each of the symbols $+$, $-$, and $\times$ to make the following math sentence true.

   5 ___ 2 ___ 6 ___ 9 = 13

# 1-7 Practice

## Problem-Solving Investigation: Guess and Check

Lesson 1–7

**Mixed Problem Solving**

**Use the guess and check strategy to solve Exercises 1 and 2.**

1. **MOVIES** Tickets for the movies are $7 for adults and $4 for children. Fourteen people paid a total of $68 for tickets. How many were adults and how many were children?

2. **AGES** Mei's mother is 4 times as old as Mei. Mei's grandmother is twice as old as Mei's mother. The sum of the three ages is 117. How old is Mei, her mother, and her grandmother?

**Use any strategy to solve Exercises 3–6. Some strategies are shown below.**

| Problem-Solving Strategies |
| --- |
| • Guess and check. |
| • Find a pattern. |

3. **SWIMMING** Brian is preparing for a swim meet. The table shows the number of laps he swam in the first four days of practice. If the pattern continues, how many laps will Brian swim on Friday?

| Day | Mon. | Tues. | Wed. | Thurs. | Fri. |
| --- | --- | --- | --- | --- | --- |
| Laps | 1 | 3 | 7 | 15 | ? |

4. **ORDER OF OPERATIONS** Use the symbols $+$, $-$, $\times$, and $\div$ to make the following math sentence true. Write each symbol only once.

8 ____ 2 ____ 1 ____ 3 ____ 4 = 5

5. **PATTERNS** Draw the next figure in the pattern.

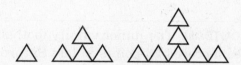

6. **MONEY** Jason has $1.56 in change in his pocket. If there is a total of 19 coins, how many quarters, dimes, nickels, and pennies does he have?

Copyright © Glencoe/McGraw-Hill, a division of The McGraw-Hill Companies, Inc.

## 1-7 Word Problem Practice

### *Problem-Solving Investigation: Guess and Check*

**1. AGES** The sum of Cooper's, Dante's, and Maria's ages is 31. Dante is twice as old as Cooper. Maria is one year older than Dante. How old are Cooper, Dante, and Maria?

**2. ELEVATION** The table shows the highest point of elevation for 5 different states. How much higher is the highest point of elevation in Colorado than Texas?

| State | Highest Point of Elevation (feet) |
|---|---|
| Arizona | 12,633 |
| Colorado | 14,433 |
| Georgia | 4,784 |
| North Carolina | 6,684 |
| Texas | 8,749 |

**3. FOOTBALL** The junior varsity football team scored 23 points in last Saturday's game. They scored a combination of 7-point touchdowns and 3-point field goals. How many touchdowns and how many field goals did they score?

**4. MONEY** Willow purchased a new car. Her loan, including interest, is $12,720. How much are her monthly payments if she has 60 monthly payments to make?

**5. PATTERNS** Draw the next figure in the pattern.

**6. FUNDRAISER** The school band is having a car wash to raise money. Their goal is to collect $150. So far they have earned $10 each from three families and $5 each from 15 families. How much more money do they have to earn to reach their goal?

## 1-8 Lesson Reading Guide

### Algebra: Equations

## Get Ready for the Lesson

**Complete the Mini Lab at the top of page 57 in your textbook. Write your answers below.**

1. Suppose the variable $x$ represents the number of cubes in the bag. What equation represents this situation?

2. Replace the bag with centimeter cubes until the scale balances. How many centimeter cubes did you need to balance the scale?

**Let $x$ represent the bag. Model each sentence on a scale. Find the number of centimeter cubes needed to balance the scale.**

3. $x + 1 = 4$

4. $x + 3 = 5$

5. $x + 7 = 8$

6. $x + 2 = 2$

## Read the Lesson

7. In the Mini Lab, how did you make the scale balance?

8. In this lesson, what makes a mathematical sentence true?

9. How are the words *solve* and *solution* related?

10. Look up the word *equate* in a dictionary. How does it relate to the word *equation*?

## Remember What You Learned

11. Suppose you are buying a soda for $0.60 and you are going to pay with a dollar bill. Write an equation that represents this situation. What does your variable represent?

Lesson 1–8

# 1-8 Study Guide and Intervention

## *Algebra: Equations*

An **equation** is a sentence that contains an **equals sign**, $=$. Some equations contain variables. When you replace a variable with a value that results in a true sentence, you **solve** the equation. The value for the variable is the **solution** of the equation.

**Example 1** Solve $m + 12 = 15$ mentally.

$m + 12 = 15$  Think: What number plus 12 equals 15?
$3 + 12 = 15$  You know that $12 + 3 = 15$.
$\quad m = 3$

The solution is 3.

**Example 2** Solve $14 - p = 6$ using guess and check.

Guess the value of $p$, then check it out.

Try 7.      Try 6.      Try 8.
$14 - p \overset{?}{=} 6$    $14 - p \overset{?}{=} 6$    $14 - p \overset{?}{=} 6$
$14 - 7 \neq 6$    $14 - 6 \neq 6$    $14 - 8 = 6$
no            no            yes

The solution is 8 because replacing $p$ with 8 results in a true sentence.

## Exercises

**Identify the solution of each equation from the list given.**

1. $k - 4 = 13$; 16, 17, 18

2. $31 + x = 42$; 9, 10, 11

3. $45 = 24 + k$; 21, 22, 23

4. $m - 12 = 15$;   27, 28, 29

5. $88 = 41 + s$; 46, 47, 48

6. $34 - b = 17$; 16, 17, 18

7. $69 - j = 44$; 25, 26, 27

8. $h + 19 = 56$; 36, 37, 38

**Solve each equation mentally.**

9. $j + 3 = 9$

10. $m - 5 = 11$

11. $23 + x = 29$

12. $31 - h = 24$

13. $18 = 5 + d$

14. $35 - a = 25$

15. $y - 26 = 3$

16. $14 + n = 19$

17. $100 = 75 + w$

# 1-8 Skills Practice

## *Algebra: Equations*

**Solve each equation mentally.**

1. $9 - m = 8$

2. $4 + k = 11$

3. $23 - x = 10$

4. $31 - h = 21$

5. $18 = 20 - b$

6. $16 + z = 25$

7. $y - 25 = 3$

8. $7 + f = 15$

9. $20 + r = 25$

10. $18 - v = 9$

11. $26 - d = 19$

12. $49 - c = 41$

13. $45 + r = 59$

14. $64 + n = 70$

15. $175 = w + 75$

**True or False?**

16. If $31 + h = 50$, then $h = 29$.

17. If $48 = 40 + k$, then $k = 8$.

18. If $17 - x = 9$, then $x = 7$.

19. If $98 - g = 87$, then $g = 11$.

20. If $p - 8 = 45$, then $p = 51$.

**Identify the solution of each equation from the list given.**

21. $s + 12 = 17$; 5, 6, 7

22. $59 - x = 42$; 15, 16, 17

23. $24 - k = 3$; 21, 22, 23

24. $h - 15 = 31$; 44, 45, 46

25. $69 = 50 + s$; 17, 18, 19

26. $34 - b = 13$; 20, 21, 22

27. $66 - d = 44$; 21, 22, 23

28. $h + 39 = 56$; 15, 16, 17

29. $54 + f = 70$; 16, 17, 18

30. $47 = 72 - b$; 25, 26, 27

31. $28 + v = 92$; 64, 65, 66

32. $56 + c = 109$; 52, 53, 54

Lesson 1-8

## 1-8 Practice

### Algebra: Equations

**Identify the solution of each equation from the list given.**

**1.** $h + 9 = 21$; 10, 11, 12

**2.** $45 - k = 27$; 17, 18, 19

**3.** $34 + p = 52$; 18, 19, 20

**4.** $t \div 6 = 9$; 52, 53, 54

**5.** $43 = 52 - s$; 8, 9, 10

**6.** $56 = 7q$; 7, 8, 9

**7.** $28 = r - 12$; 40, 41, 42

**8.** $30 \div w = 5$; 4, 5, 6

**9.** $y - 13 = 24$; 37, 38, 39

**Solve each equation mentally.**

**10.** $a + 6 = 11$

**11.** $k - 12 = 4$

**12.** $24 = 34 - j$

**13.** $9b = 36$

**14.** $f \div 7 = 8$

**15.** $7 + n = 18$

**16.** $45 \div m = 5$

**17.** $80 = 10d$

**18.** $25 - c = 15$

**19.** $17 = 9 + e$

**20.** $g \div 4 = 12$

**21.** $26 \div k = 2$

**22. ANIMALS** A whiptail lizard has a tail that is twice as long as its body. The equation $2b = 6$ describes the length of a certain whiptail lizard's tail in inches. If $b$ is the length of the whiptail lizard's body, what is the length of this whiptail lizard's body? What is the total length of the lizard?

**23. SPORTS CAMP** There are 475 campers returning to sports camp this year. Last year, 525 campers attended sports camp. The equation $475 = 525 - c$ shows the decrease in the number of campers returning to camp from one year to the next. Find the number of campers who did not return to camp this year.

# 1-8 Word Problem Practice

## Algebra: Equations

**INSECTS** For Exercises 1–3, use the table that gives the average lengths of several unusual insects in centimeters.

| Insect | Length (cm) | Insect | Length (cm) |
|---|---|---|---|
| Walking stick | 15 | Giant water bug | 6 |
| Goliath beetle | 15 | Katydid | 5 |
| Giant weta | 10 | Silkworm moth | 4 |
| Harlequin beetle | 7 | Flower mantis | 3 |

1. The equation $15 - x = 12$ gives the difference in length between a walking stick and one other insect. If $x$ is the other insect, which insect is it?

2. The equation $7 + y = 13$ gives the length of a Harlequin beetle and one other insect. If $y$ is the other insect, which insect makes the equation a true sentence?

3. Bradley found a silkworm moth that was 2 centimeters longer than average. The equation $m - 4 = 2$ represents this situation. Find the length of the silkworm moth that Bradley found.

4. **BUTTERFLIES** A Monarch butterfly flies about 80 miles per day. So far it has flown 60 miles. In the equation $80 - m = 60$, $m$ represents the number of miles it has yet to fly that day. Find the solution to the equation.

5. **CICADAS** The nymphs of some cicada can live among tree roots for 17 years before they develop into adults. One nymph developed into an adult after only 13 years. The equation $17 - x = 13$ describes the number of years less than 17 that it lived as a nymph. Find the value of $x$ in the equation to tell how many years less than 17 years it lived as a nymph.

6. **BEETLES** A harlequin beetle lays eggs in trees. She can lay up to 20 eggs over 2 or 3 days. After the first day, the beetle has laid 9 eggs. If she lays 20 eggs in all, how many eggs will she lay during the second and third days?

Lesson 1-8

## 1-8　Enrichment

## Equation Chains

In an **equation chain**, you use the solution of one equation to help you find the solution of the next equation in the chain. The last equation in the chain is used to check that you have solved the entire chain correctly.

**Complete each equation chain.**

**1.** $5 + a = 12$,　　so $a =$ _____.

$ab = 14$,　　so $b =$ _____.

$16 \div b = c$,　　so $c =$ _____.

$14 - d = c$,　　so $d =$ _____.

$e \div d = 3$,　　so $e =$ _____.

$a + e = 25 \leftarrow$ **Check:**

**2.** $9f = 36$,　　so $f =$ _____.

$g = 13 - f$, so $g =$ _____.

$63 \div g = h$, so $h =$ _____.

$h + i = 18$, so $i =$ _____.

$j - i = 9$,　so $j =$ _____.

$j \div f = 5 \leftarrow$ **Check:**

**3.** $m \div 4 = 8$,　　so $m =$ _____.

$m - n = 12$,　　so $n =$ _____.

$np = 100$,　　so $p =$ _____.

$q = 40 + p$,　　so $q =$ _____.

$p + q - 10 = r$,　so $r =$ _____.

$r - m = 8 \leftarrow$ **Check:**

**4.** $18 = v - 12$,　so $v =$ _____.

$v \div w = 3$,　　so $w =$ _____.

$80 = wx$,　　so $x =$ _____.

$w + x = 2y$,　　so $y =$ _____.

$xy - z = 40$,　　so $z =$ _____.

$z - v = 2 \leftarrow$ **Check:**

**5. CHALLENGE** Create your own equation chain using these numbers for the variables: $a = 10, b = 6, c = 18$, and $d = 3$.

## 1-9 Lesson Reading Guide

### *Algebra: Area Formulas*

## Get Ready for the Lesson

**Complete the activity at the top of page 63 in your textbook. Write your answers below.**

1. Draw as many rectangles as you can on grid paper so that each one has an area of 20 square units. Find the distance around each one.

2. Which rectangle from Question 1 has the greatest distance around it? the least?

## Read the Lesson

3. Look up the word *area* in a dictionary. Write the meaning of the word as used in this lesson.

4. In order to find the area of a surface, what two measurements do you need to know?

5. On page 63, the textbook says that the area of a figure is the number of square units needed to cover a surface. If the length and width are measured in inches, in what units will the area be expressed?

6. What unit of measure is indicated by $m^2$? How large is one unit?

## Remember What You Learned

7. With a partner, measure a surface in your classroom. Explain how to find its area. Then find the area in the appropriate square units.

Lesson 1-9

## 1-9 Study Guide and Intervention

### Algebra: Area Formulas

The **area** of a figure is the number of square units needed to cover a surface. You can use a formula to find the area of a rectangle. The formula for finding the area of a rectangle is $A = \ell \times w$. In this formula, $A$ represents area, $\ell$ represents the length of the rectangle, and $w$ represents the width of the rectangle.

**Example 1** Find the area of a rectangle with length 8 feet and width 7 feet.

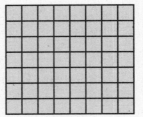

$A = \ell \times w$   Area of a rectangle
$A = 8 \times 7$   Replace $\ell$ with 8 and $w$ with 7.
$A = 56$
The area is 56 square feet.

**Example 2** Find the area of a square with side length 5 inches.

$A = s^2$   Area of a square
$A = 5^2$   Replace $s$ with 5.
$A = 25$
The area is 25 square inches.

### Exercises

**Find the area of each figure.**

1.

2.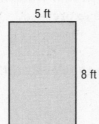
5 ft
8 ft

3.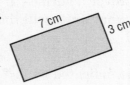
7 cm
3 cm

4.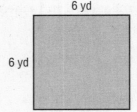
6 yd
6 yd

5. What is the area of a rectangle with a length of 10 meters and a width of 7 meters?

6. What is the area of a square with a side length of 15 inches?

# 1-9 Skills Practice

## Algebra: Area Formulas

**Complete each problem.**

1. Give the formula for finding the area of a rectangle.

2. Draw and label a rectangle that has an area of 18 square units.

3. Give the formula for finding the area of a square.

4. Draw and label a rectangle that has an area of 25 square units.

**Find the area of each rectangle.**

5.

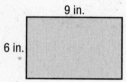

9 in.

6 in.

6.

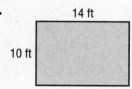

14 ft

10 ft

7.

16 cm

32 cm

8.

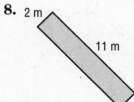

2 m

11 m

9.

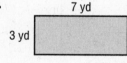

7 yd

3 yd

10.

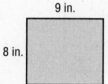

9 in.

8 in.

**Find the area of each square.**

11.

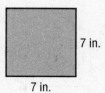

7 in.

7 in.

12.

3 cm

3 cm

13.

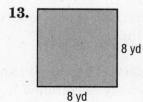

8 yd

8 yd

Lesson 1-9

## 1-9 Practice

### *Algebra: Area Formulas*

**Find the area of each rectangle.**

1.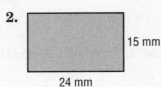

7 m

9 m

2. 15 mm

24 mm

3. 4 ft

10 ft

4. Find the area of a rectangle with a length of 35 inches and a width of 21 inches.

**Find the area of each square.**

5.

8 ft

8 ft

6. 2 cm

2 cm

7.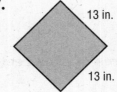

13 in.

13 in.

8. What is the area of a square with a side length of 21 yards?

**Find the area of each shaded region.**

10.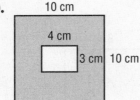

10 cm

4 cm

3 cm   10 cm

11.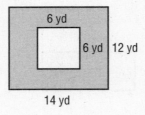

6 yd

6 yd   12 yd

14 yd

12.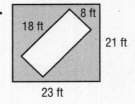

8 ft

18 ft

21 ft

23 ft

13. **REMODELING** The Crofts are covering the floor in their living room and in their bedroom with carpeting. The living room is 16 feet long and 12 feet wide. The bedroom is a square with 10 feet on each side. How many square feet of carpeting should the Crofts buy?

14. **GARDENING** The diagram shows a park's lawn with a sandy playground in the corner. If a bag of fertilizer feeds 5,000 square feet of lawn, how many bags of fertilizer are needed to feed the lawn area of the park?

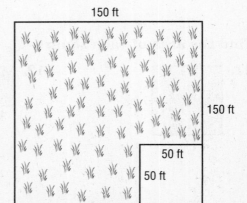

150 ft

150 ft

50 ft

50 ft

# 1-9 Word Problem Practice

## Algebra: Area Formulas

**FLOOR PLANS** For Exercises 1–6, use the diagram that shows the floor plan for a house.

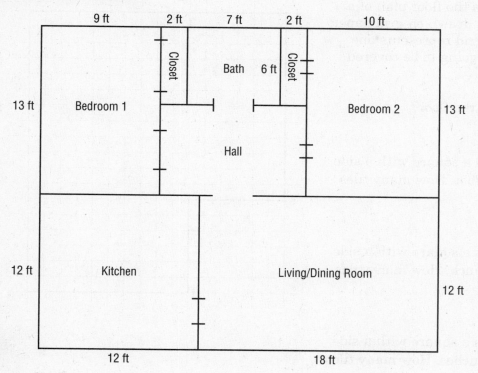

| | |
|---|---|
| **1.** What is the area of the floor in the kitchen? | **2.** Find the area of the living/dining room. |
| **3.** What is the area of the bathroom? | **4.** Find the area of Bedroom 1. |
| **5.** Which two parts of the house have the same area? | **6.** How much larger is Bedroom 2 than Bedroom 1? |

**Lesson 1-9**

## 1-9 Enrichment

### Tiling a Floor

The figure at the right is the floor plan of a
family room. The plan is drawn on grid paper,
and each square of the grid represents one
square foot. The floor is going to be covered
completely with tiles.

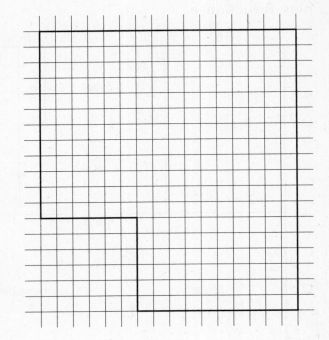

1. What is the area of the floor?

2. Suppose each tile is a square with a side
   that measures one foot. How many tiles
   will be needed?

3. Suppose each tile is a square with a side
   that measures one inch. How many tiles
   will be needed?

4. Suppose each tile is a square with a side
   that measures six inches. How many tiles
   will be needed?

**Use the given information to find the total cost of tiles for the floor.**

5. tile: square, 1 foot by 1 foot
   cost of one tile: $3.50

6. tile: square, 6 inches by 6 inches
   cost of one tile: $0.95

7. tile: square, 4 inches by 4 inches
   cost of one tile: $0.50

8. tile: square, 2 feet by 2 feet
   cost of one tile: $12

9. tile: square, 1 foot by 1 foot
   cost of two tiles: $6.99

10. tile: rectangle, 1 foot by 2 feet
    cost of one tile: $7.99

11. Refer to your answers in Exercises 5-10. Which way of tiling the floor
    costs the least? the most?

# 1-9 TI-73 Activity

## *Perimeter and Area*

Use the Equation Solver feature on the TI-73 calculator to evaluate expressions for the perimeter and the area of rectangles. The perimeter of a rectangle is given by $P = 2\ell + 2w$. The area is $A = \ell w$.

**Example 1** Find the perimeter of a rectangle whose length is 8 feet and width is 4 feet.

**Step 1** Go to the Equation Solver. Clear any existing equation.

$\boxed{\text{MATH}}$ 6 $\boxed{\blacktriangle}$ $\boxed{\text{CLEAR}}$

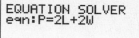

```
EQUATION SOLVER
eqn:P=2L+2W
```

**Step 2** Enter the formula for perimeter.

$\boxed{\text{2nd}}$ [TEXT] P = 2 L $\boxed{+}$ 2 W Done $\boxed{\text{ENTER}}$ $\boxed{\text{ENTER}}$

**Step 3** Enter values for L and W.

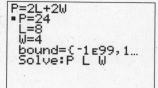

```
P=2L+2W
 •P=24
  L=8
  W=4
  bound={-1ε99,1...
  Solve:P L W
```

**Step 4** Solve for *P*.

$\boxed{\blacktriangledown}$ $\boxed{\blacktriangledown}$ $\boxed{\text{ENTER}}$

The value of the perimeter is 24 feet.
To find the perimeter of another rectangle, repeat Steps 3 and 4.

**Example 2** Find the area of a rectangle whose length is 9 feet and width is 3 feet.

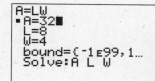

```
A=LW
 •A=32■
  L=8
  W=4
  bound={-1ε99,1...
  Solve:A L W
```

Follow the steps above, but in Step 2, enter the formula $A = \ell w$. Solve for *A*. The area is 27 square feet.

Use a graphing calculator to find the perimeter and area of each rectangle described.

1. length = 7 ft
   width = 6 ft

2. length = 8 ft
   width = 8 ft

3. length = 9 ft
   width = 2 ft

4. length = 9 ft
   width = 4 ft

5. length = 7 ft
   width = 5 ft

6. length = 6 ft
   width = 1 ft

**Lesson 1-9**

# 1 Student Recording Sheet

SCORE _____

*Use this recording sheet with pages 74–75 of the Student Edition.*

**Part 1:** Multiple Choice

**Read each question. Then fill in the correct answer.**

1. Ⓐ Ⓑ Ⓒ Ⓓ          4. Ⓕ Ⓖ Ⓗ Ⓙ          7. Ⓐ Ⓑ Ⓒ Ⓓ

2. Ⓕ Ⓖ Ⓗ Ⓙ          5. Ⓐ Ⓑ Ⓒ Ⓓ          8. Ⓕ Ⓖ Ⓗ Ⓙ

3. Ⓐ Ⓑ Ⓒ Ⓓ          6. Ⓕ Ⓖ Ⓗ Ⓙ          9. Ⓐ Ⓑ Ⓒ Ⓓ

                                              10. Ⓕ Ⓖ Ⓗ Ⓙ

**Part 2:** Short Response/Grid in

**Record your answer in the blank.**

**For grid in questions, also enter your answer in the grid by writing each number or symbol in a box. Then fill in the corresponding circle for that number or symbol.**

11. _____ (*grid in*)

12. _____ (*grid in*)

11.           12.

**Part 3:** Extended Response

**Record your answers for Question 13 on the back of this paper.**

Assessment

# 1  Rubric for Scoring Extended-Response  SCORE ____

*(Use to score the Extended-Response question on page 75 of the Student Edition.)*

## General Scoring Guidelines

- If a student gives only a correct numerical answer to a problem but does not show how he or she arrived at the answer, the student will be awarded only 1 credit. All extended response questions require the student to show work.

- A fully correct answer for a multiple-part question requires correct responses for all parts of the question. For example, if a question has three parts, the correct response to one or two parts of the question that required work to be shown is *not* considered a fully correct response.

- Students who use trial and error to solve a problem must show their method. Merely showing that the answer checks or is correct is not considered a complete response for full credit.

## Exercise 13 Rubric

| Score | Specific Criteria |
|-------|-------------------|
| 4 | An appropriate table is drawn showing that the first figure needs 6 toothpicks, the second needs 8, the third needs 10, the fourth needs 12, and the fifth needs 14. The expression $2n + 4$ is correctly identified. Complete and accurate reasoning is provided. |
| 3 | The table is correct, but one computational error in the expression is made. **OR** The computations are correct. However, the reasoning is correct but not complete. |
| 2 | The computations are correct, but the expression and reasoning are not given or are incorrect. |
| 1 | The table is incorrect. The explanation and reasoning are not given or are incorrect. |
| 0 | Response is completely incorrect. |

## 1 Chapter 1 Quiz 1

*(Lessons 1-1 through 1-3)*

**For Questions 1 and 2, use the four-step plan to solve each problem.**

1. **TRAVEL** On a trip to Florida, the Rodriguez family bought 4 adult plane tickets costing a total of $1,500. What was the cost of each ticket?

2. **MONEY** Mika saved $8 each week for 20 weeks. How much did she save in all?

3. Complete the pattern: 8, 13, 18, 23, __, __, __.

4. Is 87 *prime*, *composite*, or *neither*?

**Find the prime factorization of each number.**

5. 13                    6. 84

**Write each product using an exponent.**

7. $8 \times 8$                    8. $5 \times 5 \times 5 \times 5$

**Write each power as a product of the same factor. Then find the value.**

9. $2^3$                    10. $10^4$

1. _____
2. _____
3. _____
4. _____
5. _____
6. _____
7. _____
8. _____
9. _____
10. _____

---

## 1 Chapter 1 Quiz 2

*(Lessons 1-4 and 1-5)*

**Find the value of each expression.**

1. $3 + 12 - 9$                    2. $(7 + 4) \times 3 - 2$

3. $2^4 - 6 \div 2$                    4. $5 + 4 \times (2 + 7)$

**Evaluate each expression if $m = 3$ and $n = 7$.**

5. $n + 9$

6. $4m - 5$

7. $n^2 - 2m$

8. $3mn$

9. $20 + 8m \div 2$

1. _____
2 _____
3. _____
4. _____
5. _____
6. _____
7. _____
8. _____
9. _____

**Assessment**

1 **Chapter 1 Quiz 3**

SCORE _____

*(Lessons 1-6 and 1-7)*

**Copy and complete each function table.**

1.
| Input (x) | Output (x + 4) |
|-----------|----------------|
| 1 | ■ |
| 3 | ■ |
| 6 | ■ |

2.
| Input (x) | Output (3x) |
|-----------|-------------|
| 0 | ■ |
| 2 | ■ |
| 4 | ■ |

1. _____

2 _____

**Find the rule for each function table.**

3.
| x | ■ |
|---|----|
| 1 | 4 |
| 3 | 12 |
| 5 | 20 |

4.
| x | ■ |
|---|---|
| 2 | 0 |
| 4 | 2 |
| 7 | 5 |

3 _____

4. _____

5. **MULTIPLE CHOICE** Takeo's wallet contains 7 bills worth $28. If all of the money in his wallet are $10 bills, $5 bills, and $1 bills, how many of each bill is in Takeo's wallet?

**A.** two $10 bills, two $5 bill and three $1 bills

**B.** one $10 bill, three $5 bills, and three $1 bills

**C.** one $10 bill, two $5 bills, and eight $1 bills

**D.** two $10 bills, one $5 bill, and four $1 bills

5. _____

- - - - - - - - - - - - - - - - - - - - - - - - - - - - - - - - - - - - - - - - - - -

1 **Chapter 1 Quiz 4**

SCORE _____

*(Lessons 1-8 and 1-9)*

**Identify the solution of each equation from the list given.**

1. $a + 12 = 25$; 12, 13, 14

2. $19 = 28 - z$; 9, 10, 11

3. $3 + h = 20$; 16, 17, 18

1. _____

2. _____

3. _____

**Find the area of each rectangle.**

4.

9 ft

3 ft

5.
10 in.

11 in.

4. _____

5. _____

# 1 Chapter 1 Mid-Chapter Test

*(Lessons 1-1 through 1-4)*

## PART I

**Write the letter for the correct answer in the blank at the right of each question.**

1. **LIBRARY** At the library, 2,312 books were checked out on Friday, and 3,234 books were checked out on Saturday. Late charges of $74 and $87 were collected on Friday and Saturday, respectively. Find the total amount of late charges collected.

   **A.** $13 **B.** 5,546 **C.** 922 **D.** $161 **1.** _____

2. Write two to the fifth power using an exponent. Then find the value of the power.

   **F.** $5^2$; 25 **G.** $2 \cdot 5$; 10 **H.** $2^5$; 32 **J.** $2^5$; 10 **2.** _____

**For Questions 3 and 4, find the prime factorization of each number.**

3. 21

   **A.** $1 \times 21$ **B.** $3 \times 7$ **C.** $2 \times 10 + 1$ **D.** $2 \times 3 \times 7$ **3.** _____

4. 60

   **F.** $3 \times 20$ **G.** $2 \times 3 \times 5$ **H.** $3 \times 4 \times 5$ **J.** $2 \times 2 \times 3 \times 5$ **4.** _____

**For Questions 5 and 6, find the value of each expression.**

5. $30 \div (7 - 2) \times 2$

   **A.** 6 **B.** 10 **C.** 12 **D.** 15 **5.** _____

6. $16 - 6^2 \div 3$

   **F.** 4 **G.** 6 **H.** 7 **J.** 20 **6.** _____

## PART II

7. **TIME** A train departed at 10:15 A.M. It traveled 210 miles at 70 miles per hour. How many hours did it take for the train to reach its destination?

   **7.** _____

8. Complete the pattern: 11, 13, 15, 17, ___, ___, ___.

   **8.** _____

**Write each product using an exponent.**

9. $10 \times 10$          10. $3 \times 3 \times 3 \times 3$

   **9.** _____

   **10.** _____

**Tell whether each number is *prime, composite,* or *neither*.**

11. 0          12. 51          13. 71

   **11.** _____

   **12.** _____

14. **WALKING** Lucas can walk one mile in 12 minutes. At this rate, how long will it take him to walk 4 miles?

   **13.** _____

15. **SPORTS** A store sells baseball cards for $3 a pack and football cards for $2 a pack. Write an expression for the total cost of 5 packs of baseball cards and 3 packs of football cards. Then find the total cost of these items.

   **14.** _____

   **15.** _____

**Assessment**

# Chapter 1 Vocabulary Test

| | | |
|---|---|---|
| algebra | evaluate | power |
| algebraic expression | exponent | prime factorization |
| area | factor | prime number |
| base | formula | solution |
| composite number | function | solve |
| cubed | function rule | squared |
| definining the variable | function table | variable |
| equals sign | numerical expression | |
| equation | order of operations | |

## Choose from the terms above to complete each sentence.

1. The _____ is the small raised number in a power that tells how many times the base is used as a factor.

2. When two or more numbers are multiplied, each number is called a(n) _____ of the product.

3. The value for a variable that results in a true sentence is called a(n) _____.

4. A(n) _____ is an equation that shows a relationship among certain quantities.

5. In mathematics, a(n) _____ is a sentence that contains an equals sign.

6. The _____ is the number of square units needed to cover a surface.

7. A(n) _____ is a whole number that has exactly two factors, 1 and the number itself.

8. The word _____ means "to the third power."

9. A(n) _____ is a symbol, usually a letter, used to represent a number.

10. Numbers expressed using exponents are called _____.

1. _____

2. _____

3. _____

4. _____

5. _____

6. _____

7. _____

8. _____

9. _____

10. _____

## In your own words, define each term.

11. prime factorization

12. algebraic expression

11. _____

12. _____

# 1 Chapter 1 Test, Form 1

SCORE _____

*Write the letter for the correct answer in the blank at the right of each question.*

1. **ALLOWANCE** Juyong saves $10 of her allowance each week. Use the four-step plan to determine how many weeks she must save to buy a $40 radio.
   A. 45 weeks     B. 4 weeks     C. 40 weeks     D. 10 weeks     1. _____

2. **LAWN CARE** Luis mows lawns. The first week of spring he mowed 2 lawns. The second week he mowed 4 lawns. The third week he mowed 6 lawns. If this pattern continues, how many lawns did Luis mow the fourth week?
   F. 8     G. 12     H. 5     J. 10     2. _____

3. Find the area of the rectangle.
   A. 15 m²     C. 30 m²
   B. 2 m²     D. 50 m²

   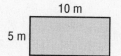

   3. _____

4. Find the next three numbers in the pattern 2, 4, 6, 8, __, __, __.
   F. 16, 32, 64     G. 10, 12, 14     H. 8, 10, 12     J. 9, 10, 11     4. _____

5. Write $3 \times 3$ using an exponent.
   A. $2 \times 3$     B. $3^2$     C. $3 \times 2$     D. 9     5. _____

6. Evaluate $2^3$.
   F. 8     G. 6     H. 9     J. 5     6. _____

7. Write $5^4$ as a product of the same factor.
   A. $5 \times 4$     B. $4 \times 4 \times 4 \times 4 \times 4$     C. $5 \times 5 \times 5 \times 5$     D. 625     7. _____

8. Evaluate $2 \cdot 4^2 - 3$.
   F. 26     G. 29     H. 61     J. 13     8. _____

9. Find the value of $5 + 7 \times 4$.
   A. 48     B. 33     C. 574     D. 39     9. _____

10. Find the value of $21 + 4 - 5 \times 2$.
    F. 81     G. 40     H. 74     J. 15     10. _____

11. Find the value of $58 - 2 \times 3 + 1$.
    A. 50     B. 53     C. 169     D. 224     11. _____

12. Find the value of $4 \times 3 + 9 \times 8$.
    F. 84     G. 168     H. 384     J. 59     12. _____

13. Evaluate $cd$ if $c = 9$ and $d = 8$.
    A. 98     B. 17     C. 72     D. 89     13. _____

**Assessment**

**14.** Evaluate $2 + 3n$ if $n = 5$.

   **F.** 37       **G.** 10       **H.** 25       **J.** 17       14. _____

**15.** Evaluate $s + t - u$ if $s = 12$, $t = 8$, and $u = 20$.

   **A.** 10       **B.** 0       **C.** 15       **D.** 18       15. _____

**For Questions 16–18, find the prime factorization of each number.**

**16.** 14

   **F.** $2 \times 7$       **G.** $1 \times 14$       **H.** $2 \times 2 \times 3$       **J.** $2 \times 2 \times 7$       16. _____

**17.** 26

   **A.** $1 \times 13$       **B.** $1 \times 26$       **C.** $2 \times 13$       **D.** $2 \times 2 \times 7$       17. _____

**18.** 200

   **F.** $2 \times 2 \times 5 \times 5$       **H.** $2 \times 100$

   **G.** $2 \times 2 \times 2 \times 5 \times 5$       **J.** $4 \times 25$       18. _____

**For Questions 19 and 20, find the rule for the function table.**

**19.**

| $x$ | ■ |
|-----|---|
| 1 | 5 |
| 3 | 7 |
| 5 | 9 |

   **A.** $x + 2$
   **B.** $x - 2$
   **C.** $x + 4$
   **D.** $x - 4$

**20.**

| $x$ | ■ |
|-----|---|
| 0 | 0 |
| 2 | 4 |
| 5 | 10 |

   **F.** $2x$
   **G.** $x \div 2$
   **H.** $3x$
   **J.** $x \div 3$

19. _____

20. _____

**21. NUMBERS** Juan is thinking of three numbers from 1 through 9 whose sum is 21. Which of the following could possibly be the numbers?

   **A.** 7, 8, and 9       **B.** 6, 7, and 9       **C.** 5, 8, and 9       **D.** 6, 7, and 8       21. _____

**22.** Which number is the solution of $x - 4 = 3$?

   **F.** 12       **G.** 1       **H.** 7       **J.** 6       22. _____

**23.** Which number is the solution of $14 = y + 4$?

   **A.** 12       **B.** 20       **C.** 18       **D.** 10       23. _____

**24.** Solve $n + 27 = 29$ mentally.

   **F.** 2       **G.** 56       **H.** 3       **J.** 55       24. _____

**25.** Solve $30 = f - 5$ mentally.

   **A.** 25       **B.** 35       **C.** 45       **D.** 150       25. _____

**Bonus** Find the greatest prime number that is less than 29.    **B:** _____

## 1  Chapter 1 Test, Form 2A

**Write the letter for the correct answer in the blank at the right of each question.**

1. **TRAVEL** A train is traveling at an average speed of 55 miles per hour. Use the four-step plan to find how far it will travel in 5 hours.
   **A.** 60 miles      **B.** 275 miles      **C.** 11 miles      **D.** 50 miles      1. _____

2. **MONEY** Amad went to the fair four days in a row. The first day he spent $2. The second day he spent $4. The third day he spent $8. If this pattern continues, how much did Amad spend on his fourth day?
   **F.** $16      **G.** $10      **H.** $12      **J.** $14      2. _____

3. Find the area of the rectangle.
   **A.** 10 cm$^2$      **C.** 21 cm$^2$
   **B.** 20 cm$^2$      **D.** 58 cm$^2$

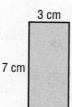
3 cm
7 cm

3. _____

4. Find the next three numbers in the pattern 17, 26, 35, _?_, _?_, _?_ .
   **F.** 44, 53, 62      **H.** 42, 55, 68
   **G.** 54, 63, 72      **J.** 52, 78, 87      4. _____

5. Write $9 \times 9 \times 9$ using an exponent.
   **A.** $3^9$      **B.** $3 \times 9$      **C.** $9^3$      **D.** $9 \times 3$      5. _____

6. Evaluate $5^3$.
   **F.** 125      **G.** 15      **H.** 243      **J.** 25      6. _____

7. Write $8^5$ as a product of the same factor.
   **A.** $8 \times 8 \times 8 \times 8 \times 8 \times 8$      **C.** $8 \times 8 \times 8 \times 8 \times 8$
   **B.** $8 \times 5$      **D.** $5 \times 8$      7. _____

8. Evaluate $4 \cdot 2^3 - 5$.
   **F.** 24      **G.** 3      **H.** 19      **J.** 27      8. _____

9. Find the value of $18 + 2 \times 3$.
   **A.** 39      **B.** 60      **C.** 23      **D.** 24      9. _____

10. Find the value of $16 - 3 + 2 \times 5$.
    **F.** 130      **G.** 23      **H.** 55      **J.** 75      10. _____

11. Find the value of $11 \times 12 + 24 \div 3$.
    **A.** 140      **B.** 52      **C.** 220      **D.** 139      11. _____

12. Find the value of $28 - 13 \times 2 + 1$.
    **F.** 11      **G.** 31      **H.** 45      **J.** 3      12. _____

**Assessment**

# Chapter 1 Test, Form 2A  *(continued)*

13. Evaluate $ab$ if $a = 91$ and $b = 8$.

    **A.** 918      **B.** 99      **C.** 728      **D.** 891      13. _____

14. Evaluate $42 - 5r$ if $r = 4$.

    **F.** 148      **G.** 41      **H.** 33      **J.** 22      14. _____

15. Evaluate $x \div y - z$ if $x = 32$, $y = 4$, and $z = 2$.

    **A.** 6      **B.** 16      **C.** 10      **D.** 34      15. _____

**For Questions 16–18, find the prime factorization of each number.**

16. 50

    **F.** $2 \times 25$      **G.** $2 \times 5 \times 5$      **H.** $1 \times 50$      **J.** $5 \times 10$      16. _____

17. 37

    **A.** $9 \times 4$      **B.** $2 \times 2 \times 3 \times 3$      **C.** $3 \times 3 \times 4$      **D.** 37      17. _____

18. 104

    **F.** $4 \times 26$      **G.** $2 \times 4 \times 13$      **H.** $2 \times 2 \times 2 \times 13$      **J.** $8 \times 13$      18. _____

**For Questions 19 and 20, find the rule for the function table.**

19.

| $x$ | ■ |
|-----|---|
| 5 | 0 |
| 7 | 2 |
| 10 | 5 |

    **A.** $x - 3$      **B.** $x - 5$      **C.** $x + 3$      **D.** $x + 5$      19. _____

20.

| $x$ | ■ |
|-----|---|
| 1 | 3 |
| 2 | 6 |
| 5 | 15 |

    **F.** $4x$      **G.** $x \div 4$      **H.** $3x$      **J.** $x \div 3$      20. _____

21. **NUMBERS** Maggie is thinking of four numbers from 1 through 9 whose sum is 33. Which of the following could possibly be the numbers?

    **A.** 6, 7, 8, and 9      **B.** 7, 8, 9, and 9      **C.** 4, 8, 9, and 9      **D.** 6, 7, 7, and 8      21. _____

22. Which number is the solution of $x + 6 = 24$?

    **F.** 4      **G.** 18      **H.** 20      **J.** 30      22. _____

23. Which number is the solution of $23 = 18 + n$?

    **A.** 5      **B.** 6      **C.** 41      **D.** 15      23. _____

24. Solve $n - 8 = 16$ mentally.

    **F.** 8      **G.** 128      **H.** 2      **J.** 24      24. _____

25. Solve $28 - x = 4$ mentally.

    **A.** 32      **B.** 24      **C.** 7      **D.** 112      25. _____

**Bonus** Find the value of the expression $8 + 3^2 \times (9 - 5) \div 2 + 10$. **B:** _____

## 1  Chapter 1 Test, Form 2B

*Write the letter for the correct answer in the blank at the right of each question.*

1. **SHOPPING** A television sells for $495 plus tax. The tax is $24. Use the four-step plan to find the total cost of the television.
   **A.** $471  **B.** $419  **C.** $529  **D.** $519

   1. _____

2. **JOGGING** Wendie decided to start training for track. The first day, she jogged 6 laps. The second day, she jogged 12 laps. The third day, she jogged 18 laps. If this pattern continues, how many laps did she jog on the fourth day?
   **F.** 22  **G.** 24  **H.** 36  **J.** 30

   2. _____

3. Find the area of the rectangle.
   **A.** 26 mm$^2$  **C.** 30 mm$^2$
   **B.** 13 mm$^2$  **D.** 109 mm$^2$

   10 mm
   3 mm

   3. _____

4. Find the next three numbers in the pattern 1, 5, 9, 13, _?_, _?_, _?_.
   **F.** 3, 7, 9  **G.** 15, 17, 19  **H.** 17, 21, 25  **J.** 19, 25, 31

   4. _____

5. Write $5 \times 5 \times 5 \times 5$ using an exponent.
   **A.** $4^5$  **B.** $5^4$  **C.** $5 \cdot 4$  **D.** $4 \cdot 5$

   5. _____

6. Evaluate $10^5$.
   **F.** 10,000  **G.** 50  **H.** 1,000,000  **J.** 100,000

   6. _____

7. Write $4^3$ as a product of the same factor.
   **A.** $4 \times 3$  **B.** $3 \times 3 \times 3 \times 3$  **C.** $4 \times 4 \times 4$  **D.** $4 \times 4 \times 4 \times 4$

   7. _____

8. Evaluate $5^2 \cdot 3 - 2$.
   **F.** 73  **G.** 28  **H.** 25  **J.** 60

   8. _____

9. Find the value of $20 - 8 \div 4$.
   **A.** 48  **B.** 3  **C.** 22  **D.** 18

   9. _____

10. Find the value of $28 + 6 \times 4 - 2$.
    **F.** 134  **G.** 50  **H.** 68  **J.** 40

    10. _____

11. Find the value of $51 - 2 \times 13 + 14$.
    **A.** 1,323  **B.** 3  **C.** 39  **D.** 651

    11. _____

12. Find the value of $42 \times 3 - 10 \div 5$.
    **F.** 23  **G.** 7  **H.** 124  **J.** 84

    12. _____

13. Evaluate $mn$ if $m = 23$ and $n = 5$.
    **A.** 115  **B.** 235  **C.** 28  **D.** 523

    13. _____

**Assessment**

## Chapter 1 Test, Form 2B (continued)

**14.** Evaluate $3 + 2m$ if $m = 6$.

   **F.** 30        **G.** 15        **H.** 29        **J.** 11        **14.** _____

**15.** Evaluate $a + b - c$ if $a = 20$, $b = 10$, and $c = 5$.

   **A.** 5        **B.** 35        **C.** 25        **D.** 22        **15.** _____

**For Questions 16–18, find the prime factorization of each number.**

**16.** 30

   **F.** $2 \times 3 \times 5$        **G.** $5 \times 6$        **H.** $3 \times 10$        **J.** $2 \times 15$        **16.** _____

**17.** 47

   **A.** $2 \times 2 \times 2 \times 2 \times 3$        **C.** $4 \times 12$

   **B.** $2 \times 23$                  **D.** 47        **17.** _____

**18.** 68

   **F.** $4 \times 17$        **G.** $2 \times 2 \times 17$        **H.** $1 \times 2 \times 17$        **J.** $2 \times 34$        **18.** _____

**For Questions 19 and 20, find the rule for the function table.**

**19.**

| $x$ | ■ |
|-----|---|
| 0 | 4 |
| 2 | 6 |
| 5 | 9 |

   **A.** $x + 4$
   **B.** $x - 4$
   **C.** $x + 2$
   **D.** $x - 2$

**20.**

| $x$ | ■ |
|-----|---|
| 3 | 1 |
| 6 | 2 |
| 12 | 4 |

   **F.** $4x$
   **G.** $x \div 4$
   **H.** $3x$
   **J.** $x \div 3$

**19.** _____

**20.** _____

**21. NUMBERS** Dante is thinking of four numbers from 1 through 9 whose sum is 24. Which of the following could possibly be the numbers?

   **A.** 5, 5, 6, and 7    **B.** 3, 7, 7, and 9    **C.** 5, 6, 6, and 7    **D.** 4, 5, 7, and 9    **21.** _____

**22.** Which number is the solution of $x - 7 = 42$?

   **F.** 29        **G.** 35        **H.** 49        **J.** 52        **22.** _____

**23.** Which number is the solution of $24 = 14 + m$?

   **A.** 10        **B.** 38        **C.** 28        **D.** 18        **23.** _____

**24.** Solve $5 + n = 14$ mentally.

   **F.** 10        **G.** 19        **H.** 8        **J.** 9        **24.** _____

**25.** Solve $36 - r = 9$ mentally.

   **A.** 4        **B.** 27        **C.** 5        **D.** 45        **25.** _____

**Bonus** Find the value of the expression $4 + 2^3 \times (8 - 5) \div 2 + 7$.   **B:** _____

**1** **Chapter 1 Test, Form 2C**

1. **SWIMMING** On Saturday, 221 adults were at the swim club. On Sunday, there were 198 adults. How many more adults were at the swim club on Saturday than on Sunday?

1. _____

2. Complete the pattern: 7, 10, 13, 16, __, __, __.

2. _____

3. Find the area of the rectangle.

16 yd

2 yd ▭

3. _____

**Write each product using an exponent. Then find the value of the power.**

4. $11 \times 11$

4. _____

5. $5 \times 5 \times 5$

5. _____

6. $10 \times 10 \times 10 \times 10$

6. _____

7. $8 \times 8 \times 8$

7. _____

**Write each power as a product of the same factor. Then find the value of the product.**

8. $3^2$

8. _____

9. $4^3$

9. _____

10. $10^5$

10. _____

11. five squared

11. _____

**Find the prime factorization of each number.**

12. 21

12. _____

13. 31

13. _____

14. 88

14. _____

15. 100

15. _____

Assessment

## 1 Chapter 1 Test, Form 2C (continued)

**Find the value of each expression.**

**16.** $5 + 20 - 7$

**17.** $8 + (29 - 11)$

**18.** $3 \times 4 - 2 \times 2$

**19.** $55 \div 5 \times 2^3$

16. _____

17. _____

18. _____

19. _____

**Evaluate each expression if $a = 3$, $b = 10$, and $c = 6$.**

**20.** $12 - b$

**21.** $2a + 5$

**22.** $2c + 3a$

**23.** $c^2 + 3a \times b$

20. _____

21. _____

22. _____

23. _____

**For Questions 24–26, find the rule for each function table.**

**24.**

| $x$ | ■ |
|-----|---|
| 1 | 3 |
| 2 | 4 |
| 4 | 6 |

**25.**

| $x$ | ■ |
|-----|---|
| 0 | 0 |
| 3 | 9 |
| 6 | 18 |

**26.**

| $x$ | ■ |
|-----|---|
| 4 | 1 |
| 8 | 2 |
| 12 | 3 |

24. _____

25. _____

26. _____

**27. MONEY** Sabrina has 6 coins that total $1.15. What are the coins?

27. _____

**Identify the solution of each equation from the list given.**

**28.** $14 + d = 20$; 6, 7, 8

**29.** $p - 11 = 17$; 26, 27, 28

28. _____

29. _____

**Solve each equation mentally.**

**30.** $j + 3 = 13$

**31.** $m - 5 = 10$

**32.** $14 - h = 12$

**33.** $20 + k = 25$

30. _____

31. _____

32. _____

33. _____

**Bonus** Find the value of the expression $36 \div 3^2 + (15 \div 3) - 8 + 1$. **B:** _____

**1** **Chapter 1 Test, Form 2D**

SCORE _____

1. **TENNIS** On Saturday, 138 adults were at the tennis club. On Sunday, there were 187 adults. How many more adults were at the tennis club on Sunday than on Saturday?

1. _____

2. Complete the pattern: 3, 7, 11, 15, ___, ___, ___.

2. _____

3. Find the area of the rectangle.

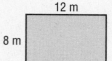

12 m

8 m

3. _____

**Write each product using an exponent. Then find the value of the power.**

4. $12 \times 12$

4. _____

5. $3 \times 3 \times 3$

5. _____

6. $10 \times 10 \times 10$

6. _____

7. $4 \times 4 \times 4 \times 4 \times 4$

7. _____

**Write each power as a product of the same factor. Then find the value of the product.**

8. $11^2$

8. _____

9. $3^3$

9. _____

10. $10^6$

10. _____

11. nine squared

11. _____

**Find the prime factorization of each number.**

12. 15

12. _____

13. 29

13. _____

14. 99

14. _____

15. 78

15. _____

Assessment

## 1 Chapter 1 Test, Form 2D *(continued)*

**Find the value of each expression.**

16. $8 + 12 - 3$

17. $7 + (31 - 10)$

18. $4 \times 5 - 3 \times 2$

19. $9 + 4^2 \div 8$

16. _____

17. _____

18. _____

19. _____

**Evaluate each expression if $x = 2$, $y = 12$, and $z = 5$.**

20. $15 - y$

21. $3z + 4$

22. $5x + 2z$

23. $x^2 + 2y + z$

20. _____

21. _____

22. _____

23. _____

**For Questions 24–26, find the rule for each function table.**

24.

| $x$ | ■ |
|---|---|
| 1 | 4 |
| 2 | 8 |
| 4 | 16 |

25.

| $x$ | ■ |
|---|---|
| 0 | 0 |
| 3 | 1 |
| 9 | 3 |

26.

| $x$ | ■ |
|---|---|
| 3 | 1 |
| 5 | 3 |
| 8 | 6 |

24. _____

25. _____

26. _____

27. **MONEY** Mia has 8 coins that total $1.10. What are the coins?

27. _____

**Identify the solution of each equation from the list given.**

28. $12 + m = 30$; 17, 18, 19

29. $k - 9 = 31$; 40, 41, 42

28. _____

29. _____

**Solve each equation mentally.**

30. $d + 4 = 14$

31. $p - 7 = 9$

32. $20 - j = 17$

33. $30 + h = 37$

30. _____

31. _____

32. _____

33. _____

**Bonus** Find the value of the expression
$32 \div 2^2 + (20 \div 5) - 10 - 2$.

B: _____

# 1  Chapter 1 Test, Form 3

1. **PIZZA** A pizza parlor sold 78 pizzas on Monday, 54 pizzas on Tuesday, and 89 pizzas on Wednesday. How many more pizzas were sold on Wednesday than on Tuesday?

1. _____

2. **MONEY** The McWilliams family wants to buy a home theater that costs $580. They plan to pay in four equal payments. What will be the amount of each payment?

2. _____

3. Find the area of the rectangle.

18 ft

9 ft

3. _____

4. **TECHNOLOGY** A computer screen measures 12 inches by 14 inches. What is the area of the viewing screen?

4. _____

**For Questions 5 and 6, write each product using an exponent. Then find the value of the power.**

5. $12 \times 12$

5. _____

6. $3 \times 3 \times 3 \times 3 \times 3$

6. _____

**For Questions 7 and 8, write each power as a product of the same factor. Then find the value of the product.**

7. $10^3$

7. _____

8. $2^6$

8. _____

9. List the factors of 56.

9. _____

10. Tell whether 37 is *prime*, *composite*, or *neither*.

10. _____

**Find the prime factorization of each number.**

11. 124

11. _____

12. 48

12. _____

Assessment

**1** **Chapter 1 Test, Form 3** *(continued)*

**Find the value of each expression.**

**13.** $22 \times (10 \div 2) + 1$

13. _____

**14.** $15 \div 5 + (3^2 - 5)$

14. _____

**Evaluate each expression if $e = 4$, $f = 9$, and $g = 5$.**

**15.** $3e + g$

15. _____

**16.** $4g + f - 2e$

16. _____

**For Questions 17–19, find the rule for each function table.**

**17.**

| $x$ | ■ |
|---|---|
| 0 | 0 |
| 2 | 6 |
| 5 | 15 |

**18.**

| $x$ | ■ |
|---|---|
| 4 | 1 |
| 12 | 3 |
| 20 | 5 |

**19.**

| $x$ | ■ |
|---|---|
| 0 | 3 |
| 1 | 5 |
| 2 | 7 |
| 3 | 9 |

17. _____

18. _____

19. _____

**For Questions 20–22, solve each equation mentally.**

**20.** $17 + h = 25$

20. _____

**21.** $16 = 29 - y$

21. _____

**22.** $45 - m = 12$

22. _____

**23.** What is the value of 50 divided by 10 times 6 minus 15?

23. _____

**24. CARS** To find the speed of a car, use the expression $d \div t$ where $d$ represents the distance and $t$ represents time. Find the speed of a car that travels 448 miles in 8 hours.

24. _____

**25.** Which of the numbers 4, 5, or 6 is a solution of $x + 5 > 10$?

25. _____

**Bonus** Derick bought party prizes that each cost the same. He spent a total of $35. Find three possible costs per prize and the number of prizes that he could have purchased.

B: _____

# 1 Chapter 1 Extended-Response Test

**Demonstrate your knowledge by giving a clear, concise solution to each problem. Be sure to include all relevant drawings and justify your answers. You may show your solution in more than one way or investigate beyond the requirements of the problem. If necessary, record your answer on another piece of paper.**

1. Name in order the four steps of the problem-solving plan. Tell what you do at each step.

2. Write the order of operations in your own words.

3. Mr. Berkowitz is planning the half-time show for the first football game of the season. He expects 120 band members this year and needs to determine possible marching formations.

   a. Tell how to find the prime factorization of a number.

   b. Find the prime factorization of 120. Show your work.

   c. Give all possible rectangular formations the band can make.

4. a. Write the rule for the function table below.

| Input ($x$) | Output ( _____ ) |
|:---:|:---:|
| 1 | 2 |
| 2 | 5 |
| 3 | 8 |
| 4 | |
| 6 | |
| 10 | |

   b. Complete the function table above.

Assessment

# 1 Standardized Test Practice

*(Chapter 1)*

## Part 1: Multiple Choice

**Instructions:** Fill in the appropriate circle for the best answer.

1. On a map of Illinois, each inch represents approximately 21 miles. Helena is planning to travel from Springfield to Chicago. If the distance on the map from Springfield to Chicago is about 10 inches, about how far will she travel? (Lesson 1-1)

   **A** 10 miles  **B** 21 miles  **C** 210 miles  **D** 21 inches

   1. Ⓐ Ⓑ Ⓒ Ⓓ

2. Find the next three numbers in the pattern 250, 275, 300, ___, ___, ___. (Lesson 1-1)

   **F** 325, 350, 375  **H** 350, 400, 450
   **G** 275, 250, 225  **J** 305, 310, 315

   2. Ⓕ Ⓖ Ⓗ Ⓙ

3. Which number is prime? (Lesson 1-2)

   **A** 4  **B** 12  **C** 15  **D** 19

   3. Ⓐ Ⓑ Ⓒ Ⓓ

4. Find the prime factorization of 20. (Lesson 1-2)

   **F** $4 \times 5$  **G** $2 \times 2 \times 5$  **H** $2 \times 10$  **J** $1 \times 20$

   4. Ⓕ Ⓖ Ⓗ Ⓙ

5. Write $3^4$ as a product of the same factor. (Lesson 1-3)

   **A** 81  **C** $3 \times 3 \times 3 \times 3$
   **B** $3 \times 3 \times 3$  **D** $3 \times 3 \times 3 \times 3 \times 3 \times 3$

   5. Ⓐ Ⓑ Ⓒ Ⓓ

6. Find the value of $2^2 + 24 \div 4 \times 2 - 7$. (Lesson 1-4)

   **F** 6  **G** 7  **H** 9  **J** 28

   6. Ⓕ Ⓖ Ⓗ Ⓙ

7. Evaluate $a + bc$ if $a = 2$, $b = 1$, and $c = 4$. (Lesson 1-5)

   **A** 6  **B** 7  **C** 8  **D** 12

   7. Ⓐ Ⓑ Ⓒ Ⓓ

8. Find the value of $2c + a - b$ if $a = 7$, $b = 1$, and $c = 4$. (Lesson 1-5)

   **F** 14  **G** 15  **H** 21  **J** 22

   8. Ⓕ Ⓖ Ⓗ Ⓙ

9. What is the rule for the function table? (Lesson 1-6)

   **A** $x - 3$  **C** $x + 3$
   **B** $3x$  **D** $x \div 3$

   | $x$ | ■ |
   |---|---|
   | 1 | 3 |
   | 2 | 6 |
   | 5 | 15 |

   9. Ⓐ Ⓑ Ⓒ Ⓓ

10. What values complete the function table? (Lesson 1-6)

    **F** 5, 7, 10  **H** 1, 3, 6
    **G** 2, 4, 7  **J** 6, 10, 16

    | $x$ | $x + 1$ |
    |---|---|
    | 0 | ■ |
    | 2 | ■ |
    | 5 | ■ |

    10. Ⓕ Ⓖ Ⓗ Ⓙ

**1** **Standardized Test Practice** *(continued)*

*(Chapter 1)*

11. **NUMBERS** Reilly is thinking of three numbers from 1 through 9 that total 18. Which of the following could be the three numbers? (Lesson 1-7)

   **A** 4, 5, and 8       **C** 4, 6, and 8

   **B** 3, 6, and 7       **D** 3, 8, and 8             11. Ⓐ Ⓑ Ⓒ Ⓓ

12. Which number is the solution of $x + 12 = 19$? (Lesson 1-8)

   **F** 6         **G** 7         **H** 8         **J** 9            12. Ⓕ Ⓖ Ⓗ Ⓙ

13. Solve $32 = 40 - m$ using mental math. (Lesson 1-8)

   **A** 72       **B** 12       **C** 8       **D** 7           13. Ⓐ Ⓑ Ⓒ Ⓓ

14. What is the area of the rectangle? (Lesson 1-9)

   **F** 17 mm$^2$     **H** 72 mm$^2$

   **G** 34 mm$^2$     **J** 145 mm$^2$             14. Ⓕ Ⓖ Ⓗ Ⓙ

9 mm
8 mm

15. What is the area of a square with side length 7 centimeters? (Lesson 1-9)

   **A** 14 cm$^2$     **C** 42 cm$^2$

   **B** 28 cm$^2$     **D** 49 cm$^2$             15. Ⓐ Ⓑ Ⓒ Ⓓ

---

### Part 2: Short Response

**Instructions:** Write your answers to each question in the space provided.

16. Evaluate $2 \times 5^2 - 3^2$. (Lesson 1-4)       16. _____

17. Solve $x + 9 = 17$ mentally. (Lesson 1-8)    17. _____

**Assessment**

# 1  Standardized Test Practice  *(continued)*

*(Chapter 1)*

18. Jasmine and 3 friends went to the skating rink. Each person rented skates for $8 and bought a snack for $3 and a soda for $2. Find the total dollars spent. (Lessons 1-1, 1-4)

18. _____

19. Find the prime factorization of 81. (Lesson 1-2)

19. _____

20. Write $2 \times 2 \times 2 \times 2 \times 2$ using exponents. Then find the value of the power. (Lesson 1-3)

20. _____

21. List the factors of 10. Then tell whether 10 is *prime*, *composite*, or *neither*. (Lesson 1-2)

21. _____

22. Write $4^3$ as a product of the same the factor. Then find the value of the product. (Lesson 1-3)

22. _____

23. Find the value of $3 + 10 \times (2 + 5)$. (Lesson 1-4)

23. _____

24. Find the rule for the function table.
(Lesson 1-6)

| $x$ | ■ |
|---|---|
| 4 | 1 |
| 7 | 4 |
| 10 | 7 |

24. _____

25. Solve the equation $20 - n = 15$ mentally. (Lesson 1-8)

25. _____

26. Find the area of the rectangle. (Lesson 1-9)

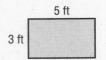
5 ft
3 ft

26. _____

27. **MUSIC** A store sells DVDs for $18 each and CDs for $14 each. (Lessons 1-2, 1-5)

   a. Write an expression for the total cost of 3 DVDs and 2 CDs.

27a. _____

   b. What is the total cost of the items?

27b. _____

## Anticipation Guide (1)

NAME _____ DATE _____ PERIOD _____

# 1  Anticipation Guide

## Algebra: Number Patterns and Functions

**STEP 1  Before you begin Chapter 1**

- Read each statement.
- Decide whether you Agree (A) or Disagree (D) with the statement.
- Write A or D in the first column OR if you are not sure whether you agree or disagree, write NS (Not Sure).

| STEP 1 A, D, or NS | Statement | STEP 2 A or D |
|---|---|---|
| | 1. An estimate is not a good indication of the answer to a problem because an estimate is not the exact answer. | D |
| | 2. To determine when an estimate can be used to answer a problem, look for words such as "about" that indicate an exact answer is not needed. | A |
| | 3. A prime number is any number with more than two factors. | D |
| | 4. $4^1$ and 4 are equivalent. | A |
| | 5. A number to the second power, such as $7^2$, is said to be *squared*. | A |
| | 6. In using the order of operations to simplify an expression, all addition and subtraction should be done first. | D |
| | 7. In using the order of operations to simplify an expression, multiply and divide in order from left to right. | A |
| | 8. In the expression $3x + 4$, $x$ is called a *variable*. | A |
| | 9. Using a guess and check strategy to solve a math problem is never a good idea. | D |
| | 10. To solve the equation $t - 5 = 12$, subtract 5 from 12. | D |
| | 11. The area of a rectangle is found by multiplying the length by the width. | A |
| | 12. The dimensions of a rectangle with an area of 12 square units must be 4 and 3. | D |

**STEP 2  After you complete Chapter 1**

- Reread each statement and complete the last column by entering an A (Agree) or a D (Disagree).
- Did any of your opinions about the statements change from the first column?
- For those statements that you mark with a D, use a separate sheet of paper to explain why you disagree. Use examples, if possible.

---

## Lesson Reading Guide (1-1)

**Lesson 1-1**

**Chapter Resources**

NAME _____ DATE _____ PERIOD _____

# 1-1  Lesson Reading Guide

## A Plan for Problem Solving

### Get Ready for the Lesson

**Read the introduction at the top of page 24 in your textbook. Write your answers below.**

1. How many purple and yellow beads are used to make one necklace?
   **40 purple beads and 16 yellow beads**

2. How many purple and yellow beads will be needed to make all eight necklaces?
   **320 purple beads; 128 yellow beads**

3. Explain how you found the number of each color of beads needed to make all eight necklaces.
   **Sample answer: I counted the number of each color beads in one set and multiplied that by 4 to find the number of each color beads in one necklace. Then I multiplied both of those numbers by 8 to find the total for all the necklaces.**

### Read the Lesson

4. Why do you think understanding the problem is so important to finding the solution? **Sample answer: You need to understand what you are looking for so that you can find the correct solution.**

5. Relate the plan step of the problem solving strategy to preparing for a trip. **Sample answer: Before going on a trip you must plan how you are going to get there, what you must pack, how long you will be gone, etc.**

6. In the four-step plan for problem solving, think about the term *check*. Does *check* come before or after the solution? (*Hint:* What are you checking?)
   **after the solution**

### Remember What You Learned

7. Think about the four steps in the problem-solving plan: Understand, Plan, Solve, Check. Write a sentence about something you like to help you remember the four words. For example, "I understand how to play chess."
   **See students' work.**

Lesson 1-1

NAME _____ DATE _____ PERIOD _____

## 1-1 Skills Practice

### A Plan for Problem Solving

**Use the four-step plan to solve each problem.**

1. **GEOGRAPHY** The president is going on a campaign trip to California, first flying about 2,840 miles from Washington, D.C., to San Francisco and then another 390 to Los Angeles before returning the 2,650 miles back to the capital. How many miles will the president have flown? **5,880 mi**

2. **POPULATION** In 1990, the total population of Sacramento, CA, was 369,365. In 2000, its population was 407,018. How much did the population increase? **37,653**

3. **MONEY** The Palmer family wants to purchase a DVD player in four equal installments of $64. What is the cost of the DVD player? **$256**

4. **COMMERCIALS** The highest average cost of a 30-second commercial in October, 2002 was $455,700. How much was this commercial worth per second? **$15,190 per second**

5. **SPORTS** A tennis tournament starts with 16 people. The number in each round is shown in the table. How many players will be in the 4th round? **2**

| | |
|---|---|
| 1st Round | 16 |
| 2nd Round | 8 |
| 3rd Round | 4 |
| 4th Round | ? |

**Complete the pattern.**

6. 2, 4, 8, 16, 32, ___ **64**

7. 16, 19, 22, 25, 28, 31, ___ **34**

8. 81, 72, 63, 54, ___ **45**

9. 5, 15, 20, 30, 35, 45, 50, ___ **60**

10. 50, 40, 45, 35, 40, 30, 35, ___, ___, ___ **25, 30, 20, 25**

11. 6, 12, 18, ___, ___, ___ **24, 30, 36, 42**

---

NAME _____ DATE _____ PERIOD _____

## 1-1 Study Guide and Intervention

### A Plan for Problem Solving

When solving problems, it is helpful to have an organized plan to solve the problem. The following four steps can be used to solve any math problem.

1 **Understand** – Read and get a general understanding of the problem.

2 **Plan** – Make a plan to solve the problem and estimate the solution.

3 **Solve** – Use your plan to solve the problem.

4 **Check** – Check the reasonableness of your solution.

**Example 1** SPORTS **The table shows the number of field goals made by Henry High School's top three basketball team members during last year's season. How many more field goals did Brad make than Denny?**

| Name | 3-Point Field Goals |
|---|---|
| Brad | 216 |
| Chris | 201 |
| Denny | 195 |

**Understand** You know the number of field goals made. You need to find how many more field goals Brad made than Denny.

**Plan** Use only the needed information, the goals made by Brad and Denny. To find the difference, subtract 195 from 216.

**Solve** 216 – 195 = 21; Brad made 21 more field goals than Denny.

**Check** Check the answer by adding. Since 195 + 21 = 216, the answer is correct.

**Exercises**

1. During which step do you check your work to make sure your answer is correct? **Check**

2. Explain what you do during the first step of the problem-solving plan. **read and get a general understanding of the problem**

SPORTS For Exercises 3 and 4, use the field goal table above and the four-step plan.

3. How many more field goals did Chris make than Denny? **6 more field goals**

4. How many field goals did the three boys make all together? **612 three-point field goals**

## 1-1 Practice
### A Plan for Problem Solving

NAME _____ DATE _____ PERIOD _____

**PATTERNS** Complete each pattern.

1. 17, 21, 25, 29, _____, _____, _____
   **33, 37, 41**

2. 32, 29, 26, 23, _____, _____, _____
   **20, 17, 14**

3. 1, 2, 4, 7, _____, _____, _____
   **11, 16, 22**

4. 64, 32, 16, 8, _____, _____, _____
   **4, 2, 1**

5. **ANALYZE GRAPHS** Refer to the graph. How many acres smaller is Lake Meredith National Recreation Area than Big Thicket National Preserve?
   **50,857 acres**

**Sizes of National Parks**

97,206
86,416
46,349
9,600
58,500

Acres: 120,000 100,000 80,000 60,000 40,000 20,000 0

Park: Amistad, Big Thicket, Guadalupe, Lake Meredith, Rio Grande Wild River

6. **TRAVEL** The distance between Dallas and Beaumont is about 290 miles. Henry drove from Dallas to Beaumont at 58 miles per hour. How many hours did it take Henry to reach Beaumont? **5 h**

7. **ANALYZE TABLES** The table lists the times that ferries leave the terminal every day. At what times will the next three ferries leave the terminal? **8:33 A.M., 8:39 A.M., 9:14 A.M.**

6:36 A.M.
7:11 A.M.
7:17 A.M.
7:52 A.M.
7:58 A.M.

8. **MONEY** The Wilsons bought a refrigerator and a stove for a total cost of $745. They will pay for the purchase in five equal payments. What will be the amount of each payment? **$149**

9. **MUSIC** Luanda practices playing the piano for 24 minutes each day. How many hours does she practice in one year? **146 h**

---

NAME _____ DATE _____ PERIOD _____

## 1-1 Word Problem Practice
### A Plan for Problem Solving

Use the four-step plan to solve each problem.

**GEOGRAPHY For Exercises 1 and 2, use the poster information about Crater Lake National Park in Oregon.**

**Visit Crater Lake National Park**

90 miles of trails
26 miles of shoreline
Boat tours available
Open 24 hours

Directions from Klamath Falls: Take U.S. Highway 97 north 21 miles, then go west on S.R. 62 for 29 miles.

1. How many more miles of trails are there than miles of shoreline in Crater Lake National Park? **64 mi**

2. How many miles is it from Klamath Falls to Crater Lake National Park? **50 mi**

3. **SPORTS** Jasmine swims 12 laps every afternoon, Monday through Friday. How many laps does she swim in one week? **60 laps**

4. **SPORTS** Samantha can run one mile in 8 minutes. At this rate, how long will it take for her to run 5 miles? **40 min**

5. **SPORTS** On a certain day, 525 people signed up to play softball. If 15 players are assigned to each team, how many teams can be formed? **35 teams**

6. **PATTERNS** Complete the pattern: 5, 7, 10, 14, _____, _____, _____ **19, 25, 32**

7. **SHOPPING** Josita received $50 as a gift. She plans to buy two cassette tapes that cost $9 each and a headphone set that costs $25. How much money will she have left? **$7**

8. **BUS SCHEDULE** A bus stops at the corner of Elm Street and Oak Street every half hour between 9 A.M. and 3 P.M. and every 15 minutes between 3 P.M. and 6 P.M. How many times will a bus stop at the corner between 9 A.M. and 6 P.M.? **25**

---

## Lesson 1-2

NAME _____ DATE _____ PERIOD _____

### 1-2  Lesson Reading Guide

*Prime Factors*

#### Get Ready for the Lesson

Complete the Mini Lab at the top of page 28 in your textbook.
Write your answers below.

1. For what numbers can more than one rectangle be formed?
**4, 6, 8, 9, 10, 12, 14, 15, 16, 18, 20**

2. For what numbers can only one rectangle be formed?
**1, 2, 3, 5, 7, 11, 13, 17, 19**

3. For the numbers in which only one rectangle is formed, what do you notice about the dimensions of the rectangle?
**The dimensions are 1 and the number.**

#### Read the Lesson

4. The word *factorization* is made up of *factor* + a verb ending + a noun ending. Write a definition for each of the following mathematical terms:

a. factor
**one of two or more numbers that are multiplied together**

b. to factorize, or to factor
**to break a quantity down into factors**

c. factorization
**the process of breaking a quantity down into factors**

5. Is 9 a prime number or a composite number? Explain.
**Composite; it has more than two factors (1 and 9, and 3 and 3).**

#### Remember What You Learned

6. Pick a number that has two or three digits. Explain to someone else how to use a factor tree to find the prime factors of the number. In your explanation, show how the rules of divisibility help you to do the factoring.
**See students' work.**

---

## Lesson 1-1

NAME _____ DATE _____ PERIOD _____

### 1-1  Enrichment

#### Using a Reference Point

There are many times when you need to make an estimate in relation to a *reference point*. For example, at the right there are prices listed for some school supplies. You might wonder if $5 is enough money to buy a small spiral notebook and a pen. This is how you might estimate, using $5 as the reference point.

- The notebook costs $1.59 and the pen costs $3.69.
- $1 + $3 = $4. I have $5 − $4, or $1, left.
- $0.59 and $0.69 are each more than $0.50, so $0.59 + $0.69 is more than $1.

So $5 will not be enough money.

**Use the prices at the right to answer each question.**

| | |
|---|---|
| Spiral Notebook Large $2.29 Small $1.59 | |
| Three-Ring Binder $4.75 | |
| Filler Paper Pack of 100 $1.29 | |
| Ball-Point Pen $3.69 | |
| Pencils Pack of 10 $2.39 | |
| Eraser $0.55 | |

1. Jamaal has $5. Will that be enough money to buy a large spiral notebook and a pack of pencils? **yes**

2. Andreas wants to buy a three-ring binder and two packs of filler paper. Will $7 be enough money? **no**

3. Rosita has $10. Can she buy a large spiral notebook and a pen and still have $5 left? **no**

4. Kevin has $10 and has to buy a pen and two small spiral notebooks. Will he have $2.50 left to buy lunch? **yes**

5. What is the greatest number of erasers you can buy with $2? **3**

6. What is the greatest amount of filler paper that you can buy with $5? **3 packs, or 300 sheets**

7. Lee bought three items and spent exactly $8.99. What were the items? **three-ring binder, pen, eraser**

8. Select five items whose total cost is as close as possible to $10, but not more than $10. **Sample answer: one pen, three packs of filler paper, one pack of pencils**

# Answers (Lesson 1-2)

---

## Left page

NAME _____ DATE _____ PERIOD _____

### 1-2 Study Guide and Intervention

#### Prime Factors

**Factors** are the numbers that are multiplied to get a product. A product is the answer to a multiplication problem. A **prime number** is a whole number that has only 2 factors, 1 and the number itself. A **composite number** is a number greater than 1 with more than two factors.

**Example 1** Tell whether each number is *prime, composite, or neither.*

| Number | Factors | Prime or Composite? |
|---|---|---|
| 15 | 1 × 15<br>3 × 5 | Composite |
| 17 | 1 × 17 | Prime |
| 1 | 1 | Neither |

**Example 2** Find the prime factorization of 18.

Write the number that is being factored at the top.

Choose any pair of whole number factors of 18.

Except for the order, the prime factors are the same.

18
18 = 3 × 6
6 = 3 × 2 → (3) × (2) × (3)

18 = 2 × 9
9 = 3 × 3 → (2) × (3) × (3)

18 is divisible by 2, because the ones digit is divisible by 2.

Circle the prime number, 2.

9 is divisible by 3, because the sum of the digits is divisible by 3.

Circle the prime numbers, 3 and 3.

The prime factorization of 18 is 2 × 3 × 3.

**Exercises**

Tell whether each number is *prime, composite, or neither.*

1. 7   **P**
2. 12   **C**
3. 29   **P**

4. 81   **C**
5. 18   **C**
6. 23   **P**

7. 54   **C**
8. 28   **C**
9. 120   **C**

10. 243   **C**
11. 61   **P**
12. 114   **C**

Find the prime factorization of each number.

13. 125   **5 × 5 × 5**
14. 44   **2 × 2 × 11**

15. 11   **11**
16. 56   **2 × 2 × 2 × 7**

---

## Right page

NAME _____ DATE _____ PERIOD _____

### 1-2 Skills Practice

#### Prime Factors

Tell whether each number is *prime, composite, or neither.*

1. 0   **N**
2. 1   **N**
3. 2   **P**
4. 3   **P**

5. 4   **C**
6. 5   **P**
7. 6   **C**
8. 7   **P**

9. 8   **C**
10. 9   **C**
11. 10   **C**
12. 11   **P**

Find the prime factorization of each number.

13. 9   **3 × 3**
14. 25   **5 × 5**

15. 28   **2 × 2 × 7**
16. 54   **2 × 3 × 3 × 3**

17. 34   **2 × 17**
18. 72   **2 × 2 × 2 × 3 × 3**

19. 55   **5 × 11**
20. 63   **3 × 3 × 7**

**SCHOOL** For Exercises 21–24, use the table below.

| Marisa's History Test Scores | |
|---|---|
| **Date** | **Test Score** |
| January 28 | 67 |
| February 15 | 81 |
| March 5 | 97 |
| March 29 | 100 |

21. Which test scores are prime numbers?   **67, 97**

22. Which prime number is the least prime number?   **67**

23. Find the prime factorization of 100.   **2 × 2 × 5 × 5**

24. Find the prime factorization of 81.   **3 × 3 × 3 × 3**

---

**Answers**

# Answers (Lesson 1-2)

NAME _____ DATE _____ PERIOD _____

## 1-2 Word Problem Practice

### Prime Factors

**ANIMALS** For Exercises 1–3, use the table that shows the height and weight of caribou.

| CARIBOU | Height at the Shoulder | | Weight | |
|---|---|---|---|---|
| | inches | centimeters | pounds | kilograms |
| Cows (females) | 43 | 107 | 220 | 99 |
| Bulls (males) | 50 | 125 | 400 | 180 |

1. Which animal heights and weights are prime numbers? **43, 107**

2. Write the weight of caribou cows in kilograms as a prime factorization. **3 × 3 × 11**

3. **ANIMALS** Caribou calves weigh about 13 pounds at birth. Tell whether this weight is a prime or a composite number. **prime**

4. **SPEED** A wildlife biologist once found a caribou traveling at 37 miles per hour. Tell whether this speed is a prime or composite number. Explain. **prime; Sample answer: Apply divisibility rules, find the prime factorization, or use a calculator to try several numbers.**

5. **GEOMETRY** To find the area of a floor, you can multiply its length times its width. The measure of the area of a floor is 49. Find the most likely length and width of the room. **7, 7**

6. **GEOMETRY** To find the volume of a box, you can multiply its height, width, and length. The measure of the volume of a box is 70. Find its possible dimensions. **2 × 5 × 7**

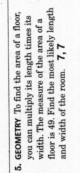

---

NAME _____ DATE _____ PERIOD _____

## 1-2 Practice

### Prime Factors

Tell whether each number is *prime, composite,* or *neither.*

1. 24 **composite**    2. 1 **neither**    3. 13 **prime**    4. 25 **composite**

5. 91 **composite**    6. 0 **neither**    7. 181 **prime**    8. 145 **composite**

Find the prime factorization of each number.

9. 16    **2 × 2 × 2 × 2**

10. 48    **2 × 2 × 2 × 2 × 3**

11. 66    **2 × 3 × 11**

12. 56    **2 × 2 × 2 × 7**

13. 80    **2 × 2 × 2 × 2 × 5**

14. 95    **5 × 19**

15. Find the least prime number that is greater than 50. **53**

16. All odd numbers greater than 7 can be expressed as the sum of three prime numbers. Which three prime numbers have a sum of 43? Justify your answer. **Sample answer: 11, 13, and 19; 11 + 13 + 19 = 43**

17. **GARDENING** Julia wants to plant 24 tomato plants in rows. Each row will have the same number of plants in it. Find three possible numbers of rows and the number of plants in each row. **Sample answer: 2 rows of 12, 3 rows of 8, 4 rows of 6**

18. **SHOPPING** Jamal bought boxes of nails that each cost the same. He spent a total of $42. Find three possible costs per box and the number of boxes that he could have purchased. **Sample answer: $2 and 21 boxes, $3 and 14 boxes, $6 and 7 boxes**

## 1-3 Lesson Reading Guide
### Powers and Exponents

NAME _____ DATE _____ PERIOD _____

### Get Ready for the Lesson

Complete the Mini Lab at the top of page 32 in your textbook.
Write your answers below.

1. What prime factors did you record? **2s**

2. How does the number of folds relate to the number of factors in the prime factorization of the number of holes?
**The number of factors is the same as the number of folds.**

3. Write the prime factorization of the number of holes made if you folded it eight times. $2 \times 2 \times 2 \times 2 \times 2 \times 2 \times 2 \times 2$

### Read the Lesson

4. Describe the expression $2^5$. In your description, use the terms *power*, *base*, and *exponent*. **Sample answer: The expression $2^5$ is called a power because it is made up of a base and an exponent. The number 2 is the base. The number 5 is the exponent.**

5. In the power $3^5$, what does the exponent 5 indicate?
**The base 3 is a factor 5 times ($3 \times 3 \times 3 \times 3 \times 3$).**

6. Complete the following table.

| Expression | Words |
|---|---|
| $4^3$ | 4 to the third power or 4 cubed |
| $7^2$ | 7 to the second power or 7 squared |
| $9^6$ | 9 to the sixth power |
| $8 \times 8 \times 8 \times 8$ | 8 to the fourth power |
| $3 \times 3 \times 3 \times 3 \times 3$ | 3 to the fifth power |

### Remember What You Learned

7. Explain how to find the value of $5^4$. **Write the power as a product ($5 \times 5 \times 5 \times 5$) and then find the value of the product (625).**

---

## 1-2 Enrichment

NAME _____ DATE _____ PERIOD _____

### Making Models for Numbers

Have you wondered why we read the number $3^2$ as three squared? The reason is that a common model for $3^2$ is a square with sides of length 3 units. As you see, the figure that results is made up of 9 square units.

$3^2 = 9$ square units

**Make a model for each expression.**

1. $2^2$     2. $4^2$     3. $1^2$     4. $5^2$

Since we read the expression $2^3$ as *two cubed*, you probably have guessed that there is also a model for this number. The model, shown at the right, is a cube with sides of length 2 units. The figure that results is made up of 8 *cubic units*.

$2^3 = 8$ cubic units

**Exercises 5 and 6 refer to the figure at the right.**

5. What expression is being modeled? $3^3$

6. Suppose that the entire cube is painted red. Then the cube is cut into small cubes along the lines shown.

a. How many small cubes are there in all? **27**

b. How many small cubes have red paint on exactly three of their faces? **8**

c. How many small cubes have red paint on exactly two of their faces? **12**

d. How many small cubes have red paint on exactly one face? **6**

e. How many small cubes have no red paint at all? **1**

7. **CHALLENGE** In the space at the right, draw a model for the expression $4^3$.

**Answers**

NAME _____ DATE _____ PERIOD _____

## 1-3 Skills Practice
### Powers and Exponents

**Write each expression in words.**

1. $7^2$ **seven to the second power or seven squared**

2. $8^3$ **eight to the third power or eight cubed**

3. $4^4$ **four to the fourth power**

4. $5^6$ **five to the sixth power**

**Write each product using an exponent. Then find the value.**

5. $4 \times 4 \times 4 \times 4$  **$4^4$; 256**
6. $3 \times 3 \times 3 \times 3$  **$3^4$; 81**

7. $5 \times 5 \times 5 \times 5$  **$5^4$; 625**
8. $7 \times 7$  **$7^2$; 49**

9. $3 \times 3 \times 3 \times 3 \times 3$  **$3^5$; 243**
10. $2 \times 2 \times 2 \times 2 \times 2 \times 2$  **$2^6$; 64**

11. $6 \times 6 \times 6$  **$6^3$; 216**
12. $6 \times 6 \times 6 \times 6$  **$6^4$; 1,296**

**Write each power as a product of the same factor. Then find the value.**

13. $3^8$  **$3 \times 3 \times 3 \times 3 \times 3 \times 3 \times 3 \times 3$; 6,561**
14. $2^5$  **$2 \times 2 \times 2 \times 2 \times 2$; 32**

15. $8^3$  **$8 \times 8 \times 8$; 512**
16. $10^5$  **$10 \times 10 \times 10 \times 10 \times 10$; 100,000**

17. $6^2$  **$6 \times 6$; 36**
18. $7^4$  **$7 \times 7 \times 7 \times 7$; 2,401**

19. $2^3$  **$2 \times 2 \times 2$; 8**
20. $3^5$  **$3 \times 3 \times 3 \times 3 \times 3$; 243**

21. $6^5$  **$6 \times 6 \times 6 \times 6 \times 6$; 7,776**
22. $2^7$  **$2 \times 2 \times 2 \times 2 \times 2 \times 2 \times 2$; 128**

**Write the prime factorization of each number using exponents.**

23. 54  **$2 \times 3^3$**
24. 36  **$2^2 \times 3^2$**

25. 63  **$3^2 \times 7$**
26. 245  **$5 \times 7^2$**

---

NAME _____ DATE _____ PERIOD _____

## 1-3 Study Guide and Intervention
### Powers and Exponents

A product of prime factors can be written using exponents and a base. Numbers expressed using exponents are called **powers**.

| Powers | Words | Expression | Value |
|---|---|---|---|
| $4^2$ | 4 to the second power or 4 squared | $4 \times 4$ | 16 |
| $5^6$ | 5 to the sixth power | $5 \times 5 \times 5 \times 5 \times 5 \times 5$ | 15,625 |
| $7^4$ | 7 to the fourth power | $7 \times 7 \times 7 \times 7$ | 2,401 |
| $9^3$ | 9 to the third power or 9 cubed | $9 \times 9 \times 9$ | 729 |

**Example 1**  Write $6 \times 6 \times 6$ using an exponent. Then find the value.

The base is 6. Since 6 is a factor 3 times, the exponent is 3.
$6 \times 6 \times 6 = 6^3$ or 216

**Example 2**  Write $2^4$ as a product of the same factor. Then find the value.

The base is 2. The exponent is 4. So, 2 is a factor 4 times.
$2^4 = 2 \times 2 \times 2 \times 2$ or 16

**Example 3**  Write the prime factorization of 225 using exponents.

The prime factorization of 225 can be written as $3 \times 3 \times 5 \times 5$, or $3^2 \times 5^2$.

**Exercises**

**Write each product using an exponent. Then find the value.**

1. $2 \times 2 \times 2 \times 2 \times 2$  **$2^5$; 32**
2. $9 \times 9$  **$9^2$; 81**

3. $3 \times 3 \times 3$  **$3^3$; 27**
4. $5 \times 5 \times 5$  **$5^3$; 125**

5. $3 \times 3 \times 3 \times 3 \times 3$  **$3^5$; 243**
6. $10 \times 10$  **$10^2$; 100**

**Write each power as a product of the same factor. Then find the value.**

7. $7^2$  **$7 \times 7$; 49**
8. $4^3$  **$4 \times 4 \times 4$; 64**

9. $8^4$  **$8 \times 8 \times 8 \times 8$; 4,096**
10. $5^5$  **$5 \times 5 \times 5 \times 5 \times 5$; 3,125**

11. $2^8$  **$2 \times 2 \times 2 \times 2 \times 2 \times 2 \times 2 \times 2$; 256**
12. $7^3$  **$7 \times 7 \times 7$; 343**

**Write the prime factorization of each number using exponents.**

13. 40  **$2^3 \times 5$**
14. 75  **$3 \times 5^2$**

15. 100  **$2^2 \times 5^2$**
16. 147  **$3 \times 7^2$**

NAME _____ DATE _____ PERIOD _____

## 1-3 Practice

### Powers and Exponents

**Write each product using an exponent.**

1. $6 \times 6$   $6^2$

2. $10 \times 10 \times 10 \times 10$   $10^4$

3. $4 \times 4 \times 4 \times 4 \times 4$   $4^5$

4. $8 \times 8 \times 8 \times 8 \times 8 \times 8 \times 8 \times 8$   $8^8$

5. $5 \times 5 \times 5 \times 5 \times 5 \times 5$   $5^6$

6. $13 \times 13 \times 13$   $13^3$

**Write each power as a product of the same factor. Then find the value.**

7. $10^1$   $10; 10$

8. $2^7$   $2 \times 2 \times 2 \times 2 \times 2 \times 2 \times 2; 128$

9. $8^3$   $8 \times 8 \times 8; 512$

10. $3^8$   $3 \times 3 \times 3 \times 3 \times 3 \times 3 \times 3 \times 3; 6,561$

11. nine squared   $9 \times 9; 81$

12. four to the sixth power   $4 \times 4 \times 4 \times 4 \times 4 \times 4; 4,096$

**Write the prime factorization of each number using exponents.**

13. 32   $2^5$

14. 100   $2^2 \times 5^2$

15. 63   $3^2 \times 7$

16. 99   $3^2 \times 11$

17. 52   $2^2 \times 13$

18. 147   $3 \times 7^2$

19. **LABELS** A sheet of labels has 8 rows of labels with 8 labels in each row. How many total labels are on the sheet? Write your answer using exponents, and then find the value.   $8^2; 64$ **labels**

20. **CANDLES** To find how much wax the candle mold holds, use the expression $s \times s \times s$, where $s$ is the length of a side. Write this expression as a power. The amount of wax the mold holds is measured in cubic units. How many cubic units of wax does the mold hold?   $s^3; 3,375$ **cubic units**

15 units   15 units   15 units

---

Lesson 1-3

NAME _____ DATE _____ PERIOD _____

## 1-3 Word Problem Practice

### Powers and Exponents

1. **SPACE** The Sun is about $10 \cdot 10$ million miles away from Earth. Write $10 \cdot 10$ using an exponent. Then find the value of the power. How many miles away is the Sun?   $10^2; 100; 100$ **million mi**

2. **WEIGHT** A 100-pound person on Earth would weigh about $4 \cdot 4 \cdot 4 \cdot 4$ pounds on Jupiter. Write $4 \cdot 4 \cdot 4 \cdot 4$ using an exponent. Then find the value of the power. How much would a 100-pound person weigh on Jupiter?   $4^4; 256$ **lb**

3. **ELECTIONS** In the year 2000, the governor of Washington, Gary Locke, received about $10^6$ votes to win the election. Write this as a product. How many votes did Gary Locke receive?   $10 \cdot 10 \cdot 10 \cdot 10 \cdot 10 \cdot 10;$ **one million votes**

4. **SPACE** The diameter of Mars is about $9^4$ kilometers. Write $9^4$ as a product. Then find the value of the product.   $9 \cdot 9 \cdot 9 \cdot 9; 6,561$ **km**

5. **SPACE** The length of one day on Venus is $3^5$ Earth days. Express this exponent as a product. Then find the value of the product:   $3 \cdot 3 \cdot 3 \cdot 3 \cdot 3; 243$ **Earth days**

6. **GEOGRAPHY** The area of San Bernardino County, California, the largest county in the U.S., is about $3^9$ square miles. Write this as a product. What is the area of San Bernardino County?   $3 \cdot 3 \cdot 3 \cdot 3 \cdot 3 \cdot 3 \cdot 3 \cdot 3 \cdot 3; 19,683$ **mi²**

7. **GEOMETRY** The volume of the block shown can be found by multiplying the width, length, and height. Write the volume using an exponent. Find the volume.   $2^3; 8$ **in³**

C   2 in.   2 in.   2 in.

8. **SPACE** A day on Jupiter lasts about 10 hours. Write a product and an exponent to show how many hours are in 10 Jupiter days. Then find the value of the power.   $10 \cdot 10; 10^2; 100$ **h**

Answers

## 1-3 TI-83/84 Plus Activity

NAME _____ DATE _____ PERIOD _____

### Exponents

You can use a graphing calculator to evaluate expressions involving exponents.

**Example 1**  Evaluate $5^4 + 6^2$.

Enter: 5 [$\wedge$] 4 [+] 6 [$x^2$] [ENTER]  661

So, $5^4 + 6^2 = 661$.

You can also use a graphing calculator to evaluate algebraic expressions that involve exponents. You store the variables' values in the memory before evaluating all of the expressions.

**Example 2**  Evaluate $x^3 + y^4$ if $x = 2$ and $y = 5$.

Enter: 2 [STO►] [ALPHA] X [ENTER] 5 [STO►] [ALPHA] Y [ENTER] [ALPHA] X [$\wedge$]

3 [+] [ALPHA] Y [$\wedge$] 4 [ENTER]  633

So, $x^3 + y^4 = 633$ when $x = 2$ and $y = 5$.

### Exercises

Evaluate each expression.

1. $6 + 3^4 + 1$
   **88**

2. $4^5 + 10^7$
   **10,001,024**

3. $7^3 - 1^9 - 2^6$
   **278**

4. $4 + 3^5 - 5 - 2$
   **240**

5. $27 - 5^2 + 7^2$
   **51**

6. $6^6 - 5^5 + 4^4$
   **43,787**

7. $9^4 + 16 \div 2^2 - 24 \div 3$
   **6,557**

8. $10^1 - 9^2 + 8^3 - 7^4 + 6^5$
   **5,816**

Evaluate each expression if $x = 6$ and $y = 3$.

9. $x^4$
   **1,296**

10. $y^5 + 2$
    **245**

11. $x^3 + 5^3$
    **341**

12. $x^3 + y^8$
    **6,777**

13. $3x^2 + y^4$
    **189**

14. $x^5 \cdot 2y^4 - 126$
    **1,259,586**

15. $xy^8$
    **39,366**

16. $5y^5 + 5x^5$
    **40,095**

17. $x^{10} - 10xy$
    **60,465,996**

18. $4xy + 2y^3 + xy - x^4 + y^{10}$
    **57,897**

19. $xy^5 + 5y + yx^5 + 5x$
    **24,831**

Chapter 1    27    Course 1

---

## 1-3 Enrichment

NAME _____ DATE _____ PERIOD _____

### The Sieve of Eratosthenes

Eratosthenes was a Greek mathematician who lived from about 276 B.C. to 194 B.C. He devised the **Sieve of Eratosthenes** as a method of identifying all the prime numbers up to a certain number. Using the chart below, you can use his method to find all the prime numbers up to 120. Just follow these numbered steps.

1. The number 1 is not prime. Cross it out.

2. The number 2 is prime. Circle it. Then cross out every second number—4, 6, 8, 10, and so on.

3. The number 3 is prime. Circle it. Then cross out every third number—6, 9, 12, and so on.

4. The number 4 is crossed out. Go to the next number that is not crossed out.

5. The number 5 is prime. Circle it. Then cross out every fifth number—10, 15, 20, 25, and so on.

6. Continue crossing out numbers as described in Steps 2–5. The numbers that remain at the end of this process are prime numbers.

7. **CHALLENGE** Look at the prime numbers that are circled in the chart. Do you see a pattern among the prime numbers that are greater than 3? What do you think the pattern is?  **Except for 2 and 3, all prime numbers are of the form $6n + 1$ or $6n + 5$.**

Chapter 1    26    Course 1

## 1-4 Lesson Reading Guide

NAME _____ DATE _____ PERIOD _____

### Order of Operations

### Get Ready for the Lesson

**Read the introduction at the top of page 37 in your textbook. Write your answers below.**

1. How much would 3 boxes of popcorn cost? 4 sandwiches?
   **$6; $16**

2. Find the total cost of buying 3 boxes of popcorn and 4 sandwiches.
   **$22**

3. What two operations did you use in Questions 1 and 2? Explain how to find the answer to Question 2 using these operations. **Sample answer: multiply the price of each item by the amount purchased. Then add the products.**

### Read the Lesson

4. The steps for finding the value of a numerical expression are listed below. Number the steps in the correct order.
   - _____ Find the value of all powers. **2**
   - _____ Add and subtract in order from left to right. **4**
   - _____ Simplify the expressions inside grouping symbols. **1**
   - _____ Multiply and divide in order from left to right. **3**

5. Using the order of operations, explain how you would find the value of $(7 + 5) \div 2^2 + 8$. **First, add 7 and 5 (12). Then, find the value of $2^2$ (4). Next, divide 12 by 4. Then add 8.**

6. How would the value of $(7 + 5) \div 2^2 + 8$ differ if you added the 8 before you divided by 4? **Following the order of operations, the value is 11. If you do the addition before the division, the value is 1.**

### Remember What You Learned

7. Using only operation symbols and grouping symbols, write the order of operations.
   **Sample answer: 1. ( ); 2. $2^2$; 3. $\div \times$; 4. $+ -$**

---

## 1-4 Study Guide and Intervention

NAME _____ DATE _____ PERIOD _____

### Order of Operations

**Order of Operations**
1. Simplify the expressions inside grouping symbols, like parentheses.
2. Find the value of all powers.
3. Multiply and divide in order from left to right.
4. Add and subtract in order from left to right.

**Example 1** Find the value of $48 \div (3 + 3) - 2^2$.

$$48 \div (3 + 3) - 2^2 = 48 \div 6 - 2^2 \quad \text{Simplify the expression inside the parentheses.}$$
$$= 48 \div 6 - 4 \quad \text{Find } 2^2.$$
$$= 8 - 4 \quad \text{Divide 48 by 6.}$$
$$= 4 \quad \text{Subtract 4 from 8.}$$

**Example 2** Write and solve an expression to find the total cost of planting flowers in the garden.

| Item | Cost Per Item | Number of Items Needed |
|---|---|---|
| pack of flowers | $4 | 5 |
| bag of dirt | $3 | 1 |
| bottle of fertilizer | $4 | 1 |

| | cost of 5 flower packs | plus | cost of dirt | plus | cost of fertilizer |
|---|---|---|---|---|---|
| **Words** | | | | | |
| **Expression** | $5 \times $4$ | + | $3 | + | $4 |

$$5 \times $4 + $3 + $4 = $20 + $3 + $4$$
$$= $23 + $4$$
$$= $27$$

The total cost of planting flowers in the garden is $27.

### Exercises

**Find the value of each expression.**

1. $7 + 2 \times 3$  **13**
2. $12 \div 3 + 5$  **9**
3. $16 - (4 + 5)$  **7**
4. $8 \times 8 \div 4$  **16**
5. $10 + 14 \div 2$  **17**
6. $3 \times 3 + 2 \times 4$  **17**
7. $80 - 8 \times 3^2$  **8**
8. $11 \times (9 - 2^2)$  **55**
9. $25 \div 5 + 6 \times (12 - 4)$  **53**

10. **GARDENING** Refer to Example 2 above. Suppose that the gardener did not buy enough flowers and goes back to the store to purchase four more packs. She also purchases a hoe for $16. Write an expression that shows the total amount she spent to plant flowers in her garden.
    **$(4 + 5) \times $4 + $3 + $4 + $16**

**Answers**

## Skills Practice

### 1-4 Order of Operations

**Find the value of each expression.**

1. $7 - 6 + 5$  **6**

2. $31 + 19 - 8$  **42**

3. $64 - 8 + 21$  **77**

4. $17 + 34 - 2$  **49**

5. $28 + (89 - 67)$  **50**

6. $(8 + 1) \times 12 - 13$  **95**

7. $63 \div 9 + 8$  **15**

8. $5 \times 6 - (9 - 4)$  **25**

9. $13 \times 4 - 72 \div 8$  **43**

10. $16 \div 2 + 8 \times 3$  **32**

11. $30 \div (21 - 6) \times 4$  **8**

12. $6 \times 7 \div (6 + 8)$  **3**

13. $88 - 16 \times 5 + 2 - 3$  **7**

14. $(2 + 6) \div 2 + 4 \times 3$  **16**

15. $4^3 - 24 \div 8$  **61**

16. $100 \div 5^2 \times 4^3$  **256**

17. $48 \div 2^3 + 25 \times (9 - 7)$  **56**

18. $45 \div 9 + 8 - 7 + 2 \times 3$  **12**

19. $18 + 7^2 \times (8 - 2) \div 3 + 8$  **124**

20. $(5^2 + 3^3) \times (81 + 9) \div 10$  **468**

---

## Practice

### 1-4 Order of Operations

**Find the value of each expression.**

1. $34 + 17 - 5$  **46**

2. $25 - 14 + 3$  **14**

3. $42 + 6 \div 2$  **45**

4. $39 \times (15 \div 3) - 16$  **179**

5. $48 \div 8 + 5 \times (7 - 2)$  **31**

6. $64 \div (15 - 7) \times 2 - 9$  **7**

7. $(3 + 7) \times 6 + 4$  **64**

8. $9 \div 8 \times 3 - (5 \times 2)$  **23**

9. $7^2 + 6 \times 2$  **61**

10. $34 - 8^2 \div 4$  **18**

11. $45 \div 3 \times 2^3$  **120**

12. $4 \times (5^2 - 12) - 6$  **46**

13. $78 - 2^4 + (14 - 6) \times 2$  **74**

14. $9 + 7 \times (15 + 3) \div 3^2$  **23**

15. $13 + (4^3 \div 2) \times 5 - 17$  **156**

16. Using symbols, write the product of 18 and 7 plus 5.  $18 \times 7 + 5$

**ART For Exercises 17 and 18, use the following information.**
An art supply store sells posters for $9 each and picture frames for $15 each.

17. Write an expression for the total cost of 6 posters and 6 frames.
$6 \times \$9 + 6 \times \$15$ or $6 \times (\$9 + \$15)$

18. What is the total cost for 6 framed posters?  **$144**

19. **SCIENCE** There are 24 students in a science class. Mr. Sato will give each pair of students 3 magnets. So far, Mr. Sato has given 9 pairs of students their 3 magnets. How many more magnets does Mr. Sato need so that each pair of students has exactly 3 magnets?  **9 magnets**

## 1-4 Word Problem Practice

### Order of Operations

**MONEY** For Exercises 1–3, use the table that shows the price of admission to a movie theater.

| Movie Theater Admission |
|---|
| Adults: $8 |
| Children (under 13): $5 |
| Matinee (before 6 P.M.): $3 |

1. Janelle (age 12) and her cousin, Marquita (age 14), go to a 7:00 P.M. show. Write an expression for the total cost of admission. What is the total cost? **$8 + $5; $13**

2. Jan takes her three children and two neighbor's children to a matinee. All of the children are under age 13. Write an expression for the total cost of admission. How much in all did Jan pay for admission? **(1 + 3 + 2) × $3; $18**

3. Connor (age 13), his sister (age 7), and Connor's parents go to a movie on Saturday night. Write an expression for the total cost. What is the total cost? **(1 + 2) × $8 + $5; $29**

4. **SOCCER** Eduardo is 16. Eduardo's dad takes him and his younger sister to a soccer match. Tickets are $17 for adults and $13 for children (18 and under). Write an expression for the total cost of the tickets. What is the total cost of the tickets? **$17 + 2 × $13; $43**

5. **MONEY** Frankie orders two hamburgers and a soda for lunch. A hamburger is $3 and a soda is $1.00. Write an expression to show how much he paid for lunch. Then find the value of the expression. **2 × $3 + $1; $7**

6. **MONEY** A store sells barrettes for $2 each and combs for $1. Shelby buys 3 barrettes and a comb. Kendra buys 2 barrettes and 4 combs. Write an expression for the amount the two girls spent all together. Find the total amount spent. **3 × $2 + $1 + 2 × $2 + 4 × $1; $15**

---

## 1-4 Enrichment

### Operations Puzzles

Now that you have learned how to evaluate an expression using the order of operations, can you work backward? In this activity, the value of the expression will be given to you. It is your job to decide what the operations or the numbers must be in order to arrive at that value.

**Sample answers are given.**

Fill in each ☐ with +, −, ×, or ÷ to make a true statement.

1. $48 \;\boxed{-}\; 3 \;\boxed{\times}\; 12 = 12$

2. $30 \;\boxed{\div}\; 15 \;\boxed{\times}\; 3 = 6$

3. $24 \;\boxed{\div}\; 12 \;\boxed{+}\; 6 \;\boxed{\div}\; 3 = 4$

4. $24 \;\boxed{-}\; 12 \;\boxed{\div}\; 6 \;\boxed{\times}\; 3 = 18$

5. $4 \;\boxed{\times}\; 16 \;\boxed{\div}\; 2 \;\boxed{-}\; 8 = 24$

6. $45 \;\boxed{\div}\; 3 \;\boxed{-}\; 3 \;\boxed{-}\; 9 = 3$

7. $36 \;\boxed{\times}\; 2 \;\boxed{\div}\; 3 \;\boxed{-}\; 12 \;\boxed{\times}\; 2 = 0$

8. $72 \;\boxed{-}\; 12 \;\boxed{\div}\; 4 \;\boxed{\times}\; 8 \;\boxed{\times}\; 3 = 0$

Fill in each ☐ with one of the given numbers to make a true statement. Each number may be used only once.

9. 6, 12, 24

$\boxed{24} \;\div\; \boxed{12} \;\times\; \boxed{6} = 12$

10. 4, 9, 36

$\boxed{4} \;-\; \boxed{36} \;\div\; \boxed{9} = 0$

11. 6, 8, 12, 24

$\boxed{24} \;\div\; \boxed{12} \;+\; \boxed{8} \;-\; \boxed{6} = 4$

12. 2, 5, 10, 50

$\boxed{2} \;-\; \boxed{10} \;\div\; \boxed{5} \;+\; \boxed{50} = 50$

13. 2, 4, 6, 8, 10

$\boxed{8} \;\div\; \boxed{4} \;\times\; \boxed{2} \;+\; \boxed{6} \;-\; \boxed{10} = 0$

14. 1, 3, 5, 7, 9

$\boxed{9} \;\div\; \boxed{3} \;+\; \boxed{5} \;-\; \boxed{7} \;\div\; \boxed{1} = 1$

15. **CHALLENGE** Fill in each ☐ with one of the digits from 1 through 9 to make a true statement. Each digit may be used only once.

$\boxed{9} \;\div\; \boxed{3} \;\times\; \boxed{8} \;+\; \boxed{7} \;\times\; \boxed{5} \;\times\; \boxed{4} \;\div\; \boxed{2} \;+\; \boxed{6} \;\times\; \boxed{1} = 100$

## 1-4 Scientific Calculator Activity

### Order of Operations

Scientific calculators follow the correct order of operations.

**Example 1** Evaluate $18 + 3 \times 2$.

Enter: 18 [+] 3 [×] 2 [ENTER =]

If the display is 24, then the calculator follows the correct order of operations. If the display is 42, use parentheses to show the operation to be performed first as in the following example.

**Example 2** Evaluate $18 + (3 \times 2)$.

Enter: 18 [+] [(] 3 [×] 2 [)] [ENTER =] **24**

The correct answer is 24.

**Exercises**

Use a calculator to find the value of each expression.
Use parentheses if necessary.

1. $112 - 4 \times 23$  **20**

2. $15 + 12 \div 2$  **21**

3. $14 + 28 \div 7$  **18**

4. $25 + 10 - 5 \div 5$  **34**

5. $200 - 10 \times 10 \times 2$  **0**

6. $12 \div 4 \times 2 + 8$  **14**

7. $20 \div 2 \times 10$  **100**

8. $114 + 10 - 9 \times 9$  **43**

9. $28 + 42 \div 7 \div 2$  **31**

10. $125 - 100 - 25 \div 5$  **20**

**CHALLENGE**

11. $24 \div 4 \times 2 + 8 \div 4 + 4$  **18**

12. $75 \div 5 \times 5 \div 10 \times 10$  **100**

---

NAME _____ DATE _____ PERIOD _____

## 1-5 Lesson Reading Guide

### Algebra: Variables and Expressions

**Get Ready for the Lesson**

Read the introduction at the top of page 42 in your textbook.
Write your answers below.

1. What does *some number* represent?
   **The total number of crayons inside the box.**

2. Find the value of the expression *the sum of two and some number* if *some number* is 14.  **16**

3. Assume you have two boxes of crayons each with the same number of crayons inside. Write an expression that represents the total number of pieces of crayons in both boxes.  **two times some number**

**Read the Lesson**

4. Look up the word *variable* in a dictionary. What definition of the word matches its use in this lesson? If classmates use different dictionaries, compare the meanings among the dictionaries.
   **Sample answer: a quantity that may assume any of a set of values**

5. The introduction uses the expression *some number*, which can also be read as "some unknown value." In the expression *some unknown value,* would the expression *value of the variable* mean the same thing?  **yes**

**Remember What You Learned**

6. Explain the difference between a numerical expression and an algebraic expression.  **Sample answer: A numerical expression contains numbers and at least one operation. It has a constant value. An algebraic expression contains numbers, at least one operation, and also variables. Until you replace variables with numbers (or a set of numbers), you cannot determine the numerical value of the expression.**

## 1-5 Study Guide and Intervention

### Algebra: Variables and Expressions

- A **variable** is a symbol, usually a letter, used to represent a number.
- Multiplication in algebra can be shown as $4n$, $4 \cdot n$, or $4 \times n$.
- **Algebraic expressions** are combinations of variables, numbers, and at least one operation.

**Example 1** Evaluate $35 + x$ if $x = 6$.

$35 + x = 35 + 6$  Replace $x$ with 6.
$\quad\quad = 41$  Add 35 and 6.

**Example 2** Evaluate $y + x$ if $x = 21$ and $y = 35$.

$y + x = 35 + 21$  Replace $x$ with 21 and $y$ with 35.
$\quad\quad = 56$  Add 35 and 21.

**Example 3** Evaluate $4n + 3$ if $n = 2$.

$4n + 3 = 4 \times 2 + 3$  Replace $n$ with 2.
$\quad\quad = 8 + 3$  Find the product of 4 and 2.
$\quad\quad = 11$  Add 8 and 3.

**Example 4** Evaluate $4n - 2$ if $n = 5$.

$4n - 2 = 4 \times 5 - 2$  Replace $n$ with 5.
$\quad\quad = 20 - 2$  Find the product of 4 and 5.
$\quad\quad = 18$  Subtract 2 from 20.

### Exercises

Evaluate each expression if $y = 4$.

1. $3 + y$  **7**
2. $y + 8$  **12**
3. $4 \times y$  **16**

4. $9y$  **36**
5. $15y$  **60**
6. $300y$  **1,200**

7. $y^2$  **16**
8. $y^2 + 18$  **34**
9. $y^2 + 3 \times 7$  **37**

Evaluate each expression if $m = 3$ and $k = 10$.

10. $16 + m$  **19**
11. $4k$  **40**
12. $m \times k$  **30**

13. $m + k$  **13**
14. $7m + k$  **31**
15. $6k + m$  **63**

16. $3k - 4m$  **18**
17. $2mk$  **60**
18. $5k - 6m$  **32**

19. $20m \div k$  **6**
20. $m^3 + 2k^2$  **227**
21. $k^2 \div (2 + m)$  **20**

Chapter 1                36                *Course 1*

---

## 1-5 Skills Practice

### Algebra: Variables and Expressions

Complete the table.

| Algebraic Expressions | Variables | Numbers | Operations |
|---|---|---|---|
| 1. $5d + 2c$ | ? $d, c$ | ? $5, 2$ | ? $\times, +$ |
| 2. $5w - 4y + 2s$ | ? $w, y, s$ | ? $5, 4, 2$ | ? $\times, -, +$ |
| 3. $xy \div 4 + 3m - 6$ | ? $x, y, m$ | ? $4, 3, 6$ | ? $\times, \div, +, -$ |

Evaluate each expression if $a = 3$ and $b = 4$.

4. $10 + b$  **14**
5. $2a + 8$  **14**
6. $4b - 5a$  **1**

7. $a \times b$  **12**
8. $7a \times 9b$  **756**
9. $8a - 9$  **15**

10. $b \times 22$  **88**
11. $a^2 + 1$  **10**
12. $18 \div 2a$  **27**

13. $a^2 \times b^2$  **144**
14. $ab \div 3$  **4**
15. $15a - 4b$  **29**

16. $ab + 7 \times 11$  **89**
17. $36 \div 6a$  **18**
18. $7a + 8b \times 2$  **85**

Evaluate each expression if $x = 7$, $y = 15$, and $z = 8$.

19. $x + y + z$  **30**
20. $x + 2z$  **23**
21. $xz + 3y$  **101**

22. $4x - 3z$  **4**
23. $z^2 \div 4$  **16**
24. $6z - 5z$  **8**

25. $9y \div (2x + 1)$  **9**
26. $15y + x^2$  **274**
27. $y^2 + 4 \times 6$  **249**

28. $y^2 - 2x^2$  **127**
29. $x^2 + 30 - 18$  **61**
30. $13y - zx \div 4$  **181**

31. $xz - 2y + 8$  **34**
32. $z^2 + 5y - 20$  **119**
33. $3y \times 40x - 1,000$  **11,600**

Chapter 1                37                *Course 1*

## 1-5 Practice

NAME _____ DATE _____ PERIOD _____

### Algebra: Variables and Expressions

Evaluate each expression if $m = 6$ and $n = 12$.

1. $m + 5$  **11**

2. $n - 7$  **5**

3. $m \cdot 4$  **24**

4. $m + n$  **18**

5. $n - m$  **6**

6. $12 \div n$  **1**

7. $9 \cdot n$  **108**

8. $n \div m$  **2**

9. $2m + 5$  **17**

10. $4m - 17$  **7**

11. $36 - 6m$  **0**

12. $3n + 8$  **44**

Evaluate each expression if $a = 9$, $b = 3$, and $c = 12$.

13. $4a - 17$  **19**

14. $14 + 2c$  **38**

15. $c \div 2$  **6**

16. $ac$  **108**

17. $c \div b$  **4**

18. $2ac$  **216**

19. $b^3 + c$  **39**

20. $19 + 6a \div 2$  **46**

21. $4b^2 \cdot 3$  **108**

22. $3c \div (2b^2)$  **2**

23. $c^2 - (3a)$  **117**

24. $ac \div (2b)$  **18**

25. **ANIMALS** A Gentoo penguin can swim at a rate of 17 miles per hour. How many miles can a penguin swim in 4 hours? Use the expression $rt$, where $r$ represents rate and $t$ represents time.  **68 mi**

26. **CLOTHING** A company charges $6 to make a pattern for an order of T-shirts and $11 for each T-shirt it produces from the pattern. The expression $11n + $6$ represents the cost of $n$ T-shirts with the same pattern. Find the total cost for 5 T-shirts with the same pattern.  **$61**

---

## 1-5 Word Problem Practice

NAME _____ DATE _____ PERIOD _____

### Algebra: Variables and Expressions

**TRAVEL** For Exercises 1 and 2, use the table that shows the distance between cities in Arizona.

**Arizona Mileage Chart**

|  | Flagstaff | Phoenix | Tucson | Nogales |
|---|---|---|---|---|
| Phoenix | 136 miles | 117 miles | 117 miles | 181 miles |
| Tucson | 253 miles | 117 miles |  | 64 miles |
| Nogales | 317 miles | 181 miles | 64 miles |  |

1. To find the speed of a car, use the expression $d \div t$ where $d$ represents the distance and $t$ represents time. Find the speed of a car that travels from Phoenix to Flagstaff in 2 hours.  **68 mph**

2. To find the time it will take for a bicyclist to travel from Nogales to Tucson, use the expression $\frac{d}{s}$ where $d$ represents distance and $s$ represents speed. Find the time if the bicyclist travels at a speed of 16 miles per hour.  **4 h**

3. **PERIMETER** The perimeter of a rectangle can be found using the formula $2\ell + 2w$, where $\ell$ represents the length and $w$ represents the width. Find the perimeter if $\ell = 6$ units and $w = 3$ units.  **18 units**

4. **PERIMETER** Another formula for perimeter is $2(\ell + w)$. Find the perimeter of the rectangle in Exercise 3 using this formula. How do the answers compare? Explain how you used order of operations using this formula.  **18 units; equal; Add inside the parentheses and then multiply.**

5. **SHOPPING** Write an expression using a variable that shows how much 3 pairs of jeans will cost if you do not know the price of the jeans. Assume each pair costs the same amount.  **Sample answer: 3m**

6. **SHOPPING** Write an expression using variables to show how much 3 plain T-shirts and 2 printed T-shirts will cost, assuming that the prices of plain and printed T-shirts are not the same.  **Sample answer: 3x + 2y**

## 1-5 Enrichment

NAME _____ DATE _____ PERIOD _____

### Using Formulas

A formula is an equation that can be used to solve certain kinds of problems. Formulas often have algebraic expressions. Here are some common formulas used to solve geometry problems. The variables in geometric formulas represent dimensions of the geometric figures.

Area (A)   Volume (V)
of a rectangle: $A = \ell \times w$   of a rectangular prism: $V = \ell \times w \times h$
of a square: $A = s^2$
of a triangle: $A = \frac{1}{2}bh$   Perimeter (P)
of a square: $P = 4s$   of a rectangle: $P = 2(w + \ell)$

$b$ = base   $h$ = height   $\ell$ = length   $s$ = side   $w$ = width

**Write the formula that would be used to solve each problem.**

1. Jack wants to put a fence around his garden to keep rabbits out. Jack's garden is square shape. Which formula can Jack use to find how much fence he needs to buy?   **P = 4s**

2. Diane's mother will replace the carpeting in their living room. The living room is rectangular in shape. Which formula can Diane's mother use to determine how much carpeting she will need to order for her living room?
**$A = \ell \times w$**

3. Victor is cleaning his aquarium, which is shaped like a rectangular prism. After he empties the aquarium and cleans the sides, he will refill the aquarium. Which formula can Victor use to determine how much water he will put back in the aquarium?   **$V = \ell \times w \times h$**

4. Joann is making a triangular flag for a school project. Which formula can she use to determine how much material she needs to buy to make the flag?
**$A = \frac{1}{2}bh$**

**Solve each problem.**

5. A tablecloth is 8 feet long and 5 feet wide. What is the area of the tablecloth?   **40 square feet**

6. Jessica wants to frame a square picture that has sides of 6 inches. How many inches of wood will she need to make the frame?   **24 inches**

7. How many cubic centimeters of packing peanuts will fit in a cardboard box that is 9 centimeters long, 8 centimeters wide, and 3 centimeters high?
**216 cubic centimeters**

8. Joaquin is painting a mural on one wall of the school's gymnasium. Part of the mural is a triangle with a base of 20 ft and a height of 8 feet. What is the area of the triangle?   **80 square feet**

---

## 1-6 Lesson Reading Guide

NAME _____ DATE _____ PERIOD _____

### Algebra: Functions

### Get Ready for the Lesson

**Read the introduction at the top of page 49 in your textbook. Write your answers below.**

1. Write an expression to represent the number of times a hummingbird beats its wings in 2 seconds; in 6 seconds; and in $s$ seconds.
**2(52); 6(52); s(52) or 52s**

### Read the Lesson

2. If you look up the word *function* in a dictionary, you might find a definition like the following: a quantity whose value depends on that of another quantity or quantities. In the function $600t$, what does the value of $600t$ depend on?   **the value of t**

3. Find the function rule for the table below. _____ **x + 3**

| Input (x) | Output (■) |
|---|---|
| 0 | 3 |
| 2 | 5 |
| 4 | 7 |

### Remember What You Learned

4. Work with a partner. Each of you should create a table like the one in Exercise 3 above. Decide on a function rule to use for the output quantities, but do not write the rule. Exchange tables with your partner. Identify the function rule that expresses the relationship between the input quantity and the output quantity.   **See students' work.**

**Answers**

NAME _____ DATE _____ PERIOD _____

## 1-6 Skills Practice
### Algebra: Functions

**Complete each function table.**

1.
| Input (x) | Output (x + 3) |
| --- | --- |
| 0 | 3 |
| 2 | 5 |
| 4 | 7 |

2.
| Input (x) | Output (3x) |
| --- | --- |
| 0 | 0 |
| 1 | 3 |
| 2 | 6 |

3.
| Input (x) | Output (x − 1) |
| --- | --- |
| 7 | 6 |
| 5 | 4 |
| 4 | 3 |

4.
| Input (x) | Output (x ÷ 3) |
| --- | --- |
| 12 | 4 |
| 9 | 3 |
| 6 | 2 |

5. If a function rule is $2x - 3$, what is the output for 3?   **3**

6. If a function rule is $4 - x$, what is the output for 2?   **2**

**Find the rule for each function table. Write the rule in the table.**

7.
| x | x − 3 |
| --- | --- |
| 10 | 7 |
| 7 | 4 |
| 4 | 1 |

8.
| x | x + 9 |
| --- | --- |
| 3 | 12 |
| 6 | 15 |
| 8 | 17 |

9.
| x | 5x |
| --- | --- |
| 0 | 0 |
| 2 | 10 |
| 3 | 15 |

10.
| x | x ÷ 2 |
| --- | --- |
| 4 | 2 |
| 6 | 3 |
| 12 | 6 |

Chapter 1     43     *Course 1*

---

NAME _____ DATE _____ PERIOD _____

## 1-6 Study Guide and Intervention
### Algebra: Functions

A **function rule** describes the relationship between the input and output of a **function**. The inputs and outputs can be organized in a **function table**.

**Example 1**  Complete the function table.

| Input (x) | Output (x − 3) |
| --- | --- |
| 9 | ▪ |
| 8 | ▪ |
| 6 | ▪ |

The function rule is $n - 7$. Subtract 7 from each input.

| Input | Output |
| --- | --- |
| 9 − 3 → | 6 |
| 8 − 3 → | 5 |
| 6 − 3 → | 3 |

| Input (x) | Output (x − 3) |
| --- | --- |
| 9 | 6 |
| 8 | 5 |
| 6 | 3 |

**Example 2**  Find the rule for the function table.

| Input (x) | Output (▪) |
| --- | --- |
| 0 | 0 |
| 1 | 4 |
| 2 | 8 |

Study the relationship between each input and output.

| Input | Output |
| --- | --- |
| 0 × 4 → | 0 |
| 1 × 4 → | 4 |
| 2 × 4 → | 8 |

The output is four times the input. So, the function rule is $4x$.

**Exercises**

**Complete each function table.**

1.
| Input (x) | Output (2x) |
| --- | --- |
| 0 | 0 |
| 2 | 4 |
| 4 | 8 |

2.
| Input (x) | Output (4 + x) |
| --- | --- |
| 0 | 4 |
| 1 | 5 |
| 4 | 8 |

**Find the rule for each function table.**

3.
| Input (x) | Output (▪) |
| --- | --- |
| 1 | 3 |
| 2 | 4 |
| 5 | 7 |

$x + 2$

4.
| Input (x) | Output (▪) |
| --- | --- |
| 2 | 1 |
| 6 | 3 |
| 10 | 5 |

$\frac{1}{2}x$

Chapter 1     42     *Course 1*

Chapter 1     **A18**     *Course 1*

## 1-6 Word Problem Practice
### Algebra: Functions

**1. DRAGONS** The Luck Dragons that live in the Enchanted Forest weigh 4x pounds when they are x years old. Write a function table that can be used to find the weights of 6-year old, 8-year old, and 10-year old Luck Dragons.

| x | 4x |
|---|----|
| 6 | 24 |
| 8 | 32 |
| 10 | 40 |

**2. ROLLER COASTER** Twelve people are able to ride the Serpent of Fire roller coaster at one time. Write a function table that shows the total number of people that have been on the roller coaster after 1, 2, 3, and 4 rides.

| x | 12x |
|---|-----|
| 1 | 12 |
| 2 | 24 |
| 3 | 36 |
| 4 | 48 |

**3. MOVIES** At the local movie theater it costs $10.00 for 2 students to see a movie. It costs $15.00 for 3 students, and it costs $20.00 for 4 students. Let the number of students be the input. What is the function rule that relates the number of students to the cost of tickets? **5x**

**4. HOMEWORK** At Elmwood Middle School, sixth graders spend 1 hour every night doing homework. Seventh graders spend 2 hours, and eighth graders spend 3 hours. Let the students' grade be the input. What is the function rule between the students' grade and the amount of time the students spend on homework every night? **x − 5**

**5. BEADS** A bead shop sells wooden beads for $3 each and glass beads for $7 each. Write a function rule to represent the total selling price of wooden (w) and glass (g) beads. **3w + 7g**

**6.** Use the function rule in Exercise 5 to find the selling price of 20 wooden beads and 4 glass beads. **$88**

---

## 1-6 Practice
### Algebra: Functions

**Complete each function table.**

**1.**

| Input (x) | Output (x + 6) |
|-----------|----------------|
| 0 | 6 |
| 3 | 9 |
| 7 | 13 |

**2.**

| Input (x) | Output (x − 1) |
|-----------|----------------|
| 1 | 0 |
| 4 | 3 |
| 8 | 7 |

**3.**

| Input (x) | Output (3x) |
|-----------|-------------|
| 0 | 0 |
| 2 | 6 |
| 4 | 12 |

**4.**

| Input (x) | Output (x ÷ 2) |
|-----------|----------------|
| 4 | 2 |
| 8 | 4 |
| 10 | 5 |

**Find the rule for each function table.**

**5.**

| x | |
|---|---|
| 4 | 1 |
| 8 | 2 |
| 16 | 4 |

x ÷ 4

**6.**

| x | |
|---|---|
| 12 | 8 |
| 13 | 9 |
| 15 | 11 |

x − 4

**7.**

| x | |
|---|---|
| 2 | 1 |
| 6 | 3 |
| 10 | 5 |

x ÷ 2

**8.**

| x | |
|---|---|
| 3 | 0 |
| 5 | 2 |
| 6 | 3 |
| 8 | 5 |
| 11 | 8 |

x − 3

**9.**

| x | |
|---|---|
| 0 | 3 |
| 1 | 6 |
| 2 | 9 |
| 3 | 12 |
| 4 | 15 |

3x + 3

**10.**

| x | |
|---|---|
| 2 | 5 |
| 4 | 13 |
| 6 | 21 |
| 8 | 29 |
| 10 | 37 |

4x − 3

**11. FOOD** A pizza place sells pizzas for $7 each plus a $4 delivery charge per order. If Pat orders 3 pizzas to be delivered, what will be his total cost? **$25**

**12. MOVIES** A store sells used DVDs for $8 each and used videotapes for $6 each. Write a function rule to represent the total selling price of DVDs (d) and videotapes (v). Then use the function rule to find the price of 5 DVDs and 3 videotapes. **8d + 6v; $58**

NAME _____ DATE _____ PERIOD _____

## 1-7 Study Guide and Intervention
### Problem-Solving Investigation: Guess and Check

When solving problems, one strategy that is helpful to use is *guess and check*. Based on the information in the problem, you can make a guess of the solution. Then use computations to check if your guess is correct. You can repeat this process until you find the correct solution.

You can use guess and check, along with the following four-step problem solving plan to solve a problem.

**1 Understand** – Read and get a general understanding of the problem.
**2 Plan** – Make a plan to solve the problem and estimate the solution.
**3 Solve** – Use your plan to solve the problem.
**4 Check** – Check the reasonableness of your solution.

**Example 1** SPORTS **Meagan made a combination of 2-point baskets and 3-point baskets in the basketball game. She scored a total of 9 points. How many 2-point baskets and 3-point baskets did Meagan make in the basketball game?**

**Understand** You know that she made both 2-point and 3-point baskets. You also know she scored a total of 9 points. You need to find how many of each she made.

**Plan** Make a guess until you find an answer that makes sense for the problem.

**Solve**

| Number of 2-point baskets | Number of 3-point baskets | Total Number of Points |
| --- | --- | --- |
| 1 | 2 | $1(2) + 2(3) = 8$ |
| 2 | 2 | $2(2) + 2(3) = 10$ |
| 2 | 1 | $2(2) + 1(3) = 7$ |
| 3 | 1 | $3(2) + 1(3) = 9$ |

**Check** Three 2-point baskets result in 6 points. One 3-point basket results in 3 points. Since $6 + 3$ is 9, the answer is correct.

**Exercise**

VIDEO GAMES Juan has 16 video games. The types of video games he has are sports games, treasure hunts, and puzzles. He has 4 more sports games than treasure hunts. He has 3 fewer puzzles than treasure hunts. Use guess and check to determine how many of each type of video game Juan has.
**5 treasure hunts, 9 sports, and 2 puzzles**

---

NAME _____ DATE _____ PERIOD _____

## 1-6 Enrichment

### Function Rules and Dot Patterns

Function rules are often used to describe geometric patterns. In the pattern at the right, for example, do you see this relationship?

1st figure: $3 \times 1 = 3$ dots
2nd figure: $3 \times 2 = 6$ dots
3rd figure: $3 \times 3 = 9$ dots
4th figure: $3 \times 4 = 12$ dots

1st → 3 dots
2nd → 6 dots
3rd → 9 dots
4th → 12 dots

So the "*n*th" figure in this pattern would have $3 \times n$, or $3n$, dots. A function rule that describes the pattern is $3n$.

**Write a function rule to describe each dot pattern.**

1. $4n$
2. $n + 3$
3. $3n - 1$
4. $n^2$
5. $n^2 + 1$
6. $n^2 + n$ or $n(n + 1)$

7. CHALLENGE Create your own dot pattern. Then exchange patterns with a classmate. Try to find the function rule for each other's patterns. **Answers will vary.**

## Left Page

NAME _____ DATE _____ PERIOD _____

### 1-7 Skills Practice

**Problem-Solving Investigation: Guess and Check**

Use the guess and check strategy to solve each problem.

1. **MONEY** Keegan has 10 coins in his pocket that total $2.05. He only has quarters and dimes. How many of each coin does Keegan have? **7 quarters and 3 dimes**

2. **NUMBERS** Ms. Junkin told her students that she was thinking of three numbers between 1 and 9 that had a sum of 19. Find the three possible numbers. **5, 6, and 8**

3. **SHOPPING** Natasha bought some bracelets and some rings during a jewelry store sale. Each bracelet cost $4 and each ring cost $7. If Natasha spent $29 on the jewelry, how many bracelets and rings did she buy? **2 bracelets and 3 rings**

4. **ORDER OF OPERATIONS** Use each of the symbols +, −, and × to make the following math sentence true.
5 ___ 2 ___ 6 ___ 9 = 13

## Right Page

NAME _____ DATE _____ PERIOD _____

### 1-7 Practice

**Problem-Solving Investigation: Guess and Check**

**Mixed Problem Solving**

Use the guess and check strategy to solve Exercises 1 and 2.

1. **MOVIES** Tickets for the movies are $7 for adults and $4 for children. Fourteen people paid a total of $68 for tickets. How many were adults and how many were children? **4 adults and 10 children**

2. **AGES** Mei's mother is 4 times as old as Mei. Mei's grandmother is twice as old as Mei's mother. The sum of the three ages is 117. How old is Mei, her mother, and her grandmother? **Mei: 9 years old; mother: 36 years old; grandmother: 72 years old**

Use any strategy to solve Exercises 3–6. Some strategies are shown below.

| Problem-Solving Strategies |
| --- |
| • Guess and check. |
| • Find a pattern. |

3. **SWIMMING** Brian is preparing for a swim meet. The table shows the number of laps he swam in the first four days of practice. If the pattern continues, how many laps will Brian swim on Friday?

| Day | Mon. | Tues. | Wed. | Thurs. | Fri. |
| --- | --- | --- | --- | --- | --- |
| Laps | 1 | 3 | 7 | 15 | ? |

**31 laps**

4. **ORDER OF OPERATIONS** Use the symbols +, −, ×, and ÷ to make the following math sentence true. Write each symbol only once. $8 \div 2 - 1 \times 3 + 4 = 5$
8 ___ 2 ___ 1 ___ 3 ___ 4 = 5

5. **PATTERNS** Draw the next figure in the pattern.

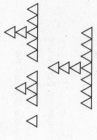

6. **MONEY** Jason has $1.56 in change in his pocket. If there is a total of 19 coins, how many quarters, dimes, nickels, and pennies does he have? **3 quarters, 5 dimes, 5 nickels, and 6 pennies**

## Lesson 1-8

### 1-8 Lesson Reading Guide

*Algebra: Equations*

**Get Ready for the Lesson**

Complete the Mini Lab at the top of page 57 in your textbook. Write your answers below.

1. Suppose the variable $x$ represents the number of cubes in the bag. What equation represents this situation? $3 + x = 8$

2. Replace the bag with centimeter cubes until the scale balances. How many centimeter cubes did you need to balance the scale? **5**

Let $x$ represent the bag. Model each sentence on a scale. Find the number of centimeter cubes needed to balance the scale. **3–6.** **See students' work.**

3. $x + 1 = 4$   **3**     4. $x + 3 = 5$   **2**

5. $x + 7 = 8$   **1**     6. $x + 2 = 2$   **0**

**Read the Lesson**

7. In the Mini Lab, how did you make the scale balance? **placed the same number of centimeter cubes on both sides of the scale**

8. In this lesson, what makes a mathematical sentence true? **when the values on both sides of the equals sign are the same**

9. How are the words *solve* and *solution* related?
**Sample answer: When you solve a problem, you find a solution.**

10. Look up the word *equate* in a dictionary. How does it relate to the word *equation*? **Sample answer: The word *equate* means "to make equal." An equation shows that two values are equal; the two values are connected by an equals sign.**

**Remember What You Learned**

11. Suppose you are buying a soda for $0.60 and you are going to pay with a dollar bill. Write an equation that represents this situation. What does your variable represent? **Sample answer: $1.00 − 0.60 = c$; $c$ represents the change from the transaction.**

---

## Lesson 1-7

### 1-7 Word Problem Practice

*Problem-Solving Investigation: Guess and Check*

1. **AGES** The sum of Cooper's, Dante's, and Maria's ages is 31. Dante is twice as old as Cooper. Maria is one year older than Dante. How old are Cooper, Dante, and Maria?
**Cooper: 6; Dante: 12; Maria: 13**

2. **ELEVATION** The table shows the highest point of elevation for 5 different states. How much higher is the highest point of elevation in Colorado than Texas?

| State | Highest Point of Elevation (feet) |
|---|---|
| Arizona | 12,633 |
| Colorado | 14,433 |
| Georgia | 4,784 |
| North Carolina | 6,684 |
| Texas | 8,749 |

**5,684 ft**

3. **FOOTBALL** The junior varsity football team scored 23 points in last Saturday's game. They scored a combination of 7-point touchdowns and 3-point field goals. How many touchdowns and how many field goals did they score?
**2 touchdowns and 3 field goals**

4. **MONEY** Willow purchased a new car. Her loan, including interest, is $12,720. How much are her monthly payments if she has 60 monthly payments to make?
**$212**

5. **PATTERNS** Draw the next figure in the pattern.

6. **FUNDRAISER** The school band is having a car wash to raise money. Their goal is to collect $150. So far they have earned $10 each from three families and $5 each from 15 families. How much more money do they have to earn to reach their goal?
**$45**

## Study Guide and Intervention (1-8)

NAME _____ DATE _____ PERIOD _____

# 1-8 Study Guide and Intervention

## Algebra: Equations

An **equation** is a sentence that contains an **equals sign**, =. Some equations contain variables. When you replace a variable with a value that results in a true sentence, you **solve** the equation. The value for the variable is the **solution** of the equation.

**Example 1**  Solve $m + 12 = 15$ mentally.

$m + 12 = 15$   Think: What number plus 12 equals 15?
$3 + 12 = 15$   You know that $12 + 3 = 15$.
$m = 3$

The solution is 3.

**Example 2**  Solve $14 - p = 6$ using guess and check.

Guess the value of $p$, then check it out.

| Try 7. | Try 6. | Try 8. |
|---|---|---|
| $14 - p \stackrel{?}{=} 6$ | $14 - p \stackrel{?}{=} 6$ | $14 - p \stackrel{?}{=} 6$ |
| $14 - 7 \stackrel{?}{=} 6$ | $14 - 6 \stackrel{?}{=} 6$ | $14 - 8 \stackrel{?}{=} 6$ |
| no | no | yes |

The solution is 8 because replacing $p$ with 8 results in a true sentence.

**Exercises**

Identify the solution of each equation from the list given.

1. $k - 4 = 13$; 16, 17, 18   **17**
2. $31 + x = 42$; 9, 10, 11   **11**
3. $45 = 24 + k$; 21, 22, 23   **21**
4. $m - 12 = 15$;   27, 28, 29   **27**
5. $88 = 41 + s$; 46, 47, 48   **47**
6. $34 - b = 17$; 16, 17, 18   **17**
7. $69 - j = 44$; 25, 26, 27   **25**
8. $h + 19 = 56$; 36, 37, 38   **37**

Solve each equation mentally.

9. $j + 3 = 9$  **6**
10. $m - 5 = 11$  **16**
11. $23 + x = 29$  **6**
12. $31 - h = 24$  **7**
13. $18 = 5 + d$  **13**
14. $35 - a = 25$  **10**
15. $y - 26 = 3$  **29**
16. $14 + n = 19$  **5**
17. $100 = 75 + w$  **25**

Chapter 1    52    Course 1

---

## Skills Practice (1-8)

NAME _____ DATE _____ PERIOD _____

# 1-8 Skills Practice

## Algebra: Equations

Solve each equation mentally.

1. $9 - m = 8$  **1**
2. $4 + k = 11$  **7**
3. $23 - x = 10$  **13**
4. $31 - h = 21$  **10**
5. $18 = 20 - b$  **2**
6. $16 + z = 25$  **9**
7. $y - 25 = 3$  **28**
8. $7 + f = 15$  **8**
9. $20 + r = 25$  **5**
10. $18 - v = 9$  **9**
11. $26 - d = 19$  **7**
12. $49 - c = 41$  **8**
13. $45 + r = 59$  **14**
14. $64 + n = 70$  **6**
15. $175 = w + 75$  **100**

**True or False?**

16. If $31 + h = 50$, then $h = 29$.  **false**
17. If $48 = 40 + k$, then $k = 8$.  **true**
18. If $17 - x = 9$, then $x = 7$.  **false**
19. If $98 - g = 87$, then $g = 11$.  **true**
20. If $p - 8 = 45$, then $p = 51$.  **false**

Identify the solution of each equation from the list given.

21. $s + 12 = 17$; 5, 6, 7  **5**
22. $59 - x = 42$; 15, 16, 17  **17**
23. $24 - k = 3$; 21, 22, 23  **21**
24. $h - 15 = 31$; 44, 45, 46  **46**
25. $69 = 50 + s$; 17, 18, 19  **19**
26. $34 - b = 13$; 20, 21, 22  **21**
27. $66 - d = 44$; 21, 22, 23  **22**
28. $h + 39 = 56$; 15, 16, 17  **17**
29. $54 + f = 70$; 16, 17, 18  **16**
30. $47 = 72 - b$; 25, 26, 27  **25**
31. $28 + v = 92$; 64, 65, 66  **64**
32. $56 + c = 109$; 52, 53, 54  **53**

Chapter 1    53    Course 1

NAME _____ DATE _____ PERIOD _____

## 1-8 Word Problem Practice

### Algebra: Equations

**INSECTS** For Exercises 1–3, use the table that gives the average lengths of several unusual insects in centimeters.

| Insect | Length (cm) | Insect | Length (cm) |
|---|---|---|---|
| Walking stick | 15 | Giant water bug | 6 |
| Goliath beetle | 15 | Katydid | 5 |
| Giant weta | 10 | Silkworm moth | 4 |
| Harlequin beetle | 7 | Flower mantis | 3 |

1. The equation $15 - x = 12$ gives the difference in length between a walking stick and one other insect. If $x$ is the other insect, which insect is it? **flower mantis**

2. The equation $7 + y = 13$ gives the length of a Harlequin beetle and one other insect. If $y$ is the other insect, which insect makes the equation a true sentence? **giant water bug**

3. Bradley found a silkworm moth that was 2 centimeters longer than average. The equation $m - 4 = 2$ represents this situation. Find the length of the silkworm moth that Bradley found. **$m = 6$ cm**

4. **BUTTERFLIES** A Monarch butterfly flies about 80 miles per day. So far it has flown 60 miles. In the equation $80 - m = 60$, $m$ represents the number of miles it has yet to fly that day. Find the solution to the equation. **20 mi**

5. **CICADAS** The nymphs of some cicada can live among tree roots for 17 years before they develop into adults. One nymph developed into an adult after only 13 years. The equation $17 - x = 13$ describes the number of years less than 17 that it lived as a nymph. Find the value of $x$ in the equation to tell how many years less than 17 years it lived as a nymph. **4 years less**

6. **BEETLES** A harlequin beetle lays eggs in trees. She can lay up to 20 eggs over 2 or 3 days. After the first day, the beetle has laid 9 eggs. If she lays 20 eggs in all, how many eggs will she lay during the second and third days? **11 eggs**

---

NAME _____ DATE _____ PERIOD _____

## 1-8 Practice

### Algebra: Equations

**Identify the solution of each equation from the list given.**

1. $h + 9 = 21$; 10, 11, 12  **12**

2. $45 - k = 27$; 17, 18, 19  **18**

3. $34 + p = 52$; 18, 19, 20  **18**

4. $t + 6 = 9$; 52, 53, 54  **54**

5. $43 = 52 - s$; 8, 9, 10  **9**

6. $56 = 7q$; 7, 8, 9  **8**

7. $28 = r - 12$; 40, 41, 42  **40**

8. $30 \div w = 5$; 4, 5, 6  **6**

9. $y - 13 = 24$; 37, 38, 39  **37**

**Solve each equation mentally.**

10. $a + 6 = 11$  **5**

11. $k - 12 = 4$  **16**

12. $24 = 34 - j$  **10**

13. $9b = 36$  **4**

14. $f \div 7 = 8$  **56**

15. $7 + n = 18$  **11**

16. $45 \div m = 5$  **9**

17. $80 = 10d$  **8**

18. $25 - c = 15$  **10**

19. $17 = 9 + e$  **8**

20. $g \div 4 = 12$  **48**

21. $26 \div k = 2$  **13**

22. **ANIMALS** A whiptail lizard has a tail that is twice as long as its body. The equation $2b = 6$ describes the length of a certain whiptail lizard's tail in inches. If $b$ is the length of the whiptail lizard's body, what is the length of this whiptail lizard's body? What is the total length of the lizard? **3 inches; 9 inches**

23. **SPORTS CAMP** There are 475 campers returning to sports camp this year. Last year, 525 campers attended sports camp. The equation $475 = 525 - c$ shows the decrease in the number of campers returning to camp from one year to the next. Find the number of campers who did not return to camp this year. **50 campers**

---

## 1-9 Lesson Reading Guide

NAME _____ DATE _____ PERIOD _____

### Algebra: Area Formulas

### Get Ready for the Lesson

Complete the activity at the top of page 63 in your textbook. Write your answers below.

1. Draw as many rectangles as you can on grid paper so that each one has an area of 20 square units. Find the distance around each one.
**4 × 5 rectangle: 18 units; 1 × 20 rectangle: 42 units; 20 × 1 rectangle: 42 units; 2 × 10 rectangle: 24 units; 10 × 2 rectangle: 24 units**

2. Which rectangle from Question 1 has the greatest distance around it? the least?
**1 × 20 rectangle and the 20 × 1 rectangle; the 4 × 5 rectangle**

### Read the Lesson

3. Look up the word *area* in a dictionary. Write the meaning of the word as used in this lesson.
**Sample answer: the number of square units equal in measure to the surface**

4. In order to find the area of a surface, what two measurements do you need to know? **the length and the width**

5. On page 63, the textbook says that the area of a figure is the number of square units needed to cover a surface. If the length and width are measured in inches, in what units will the area be expressed? **square inches**

6. What unit of measure is indicated by m²? How large is one unit?
**a square meter; a square that measures 1 meter on each side**

### Remember What You Learned

7. With a partner, measure a surface in your classroom. Explain how to find its area. Then find the area in the appropriate square units. **See students' work.**

---

## 1-8 Enrichment

NAME _____ DATE _____ PERIOD _____

### Equation Chains

In an equation chain, you use the solution of one equation to help you find the solution of the next equation in the chain. The last equation in the chain is used to check that you have solved the entire chain correctly.

**Complete each equation chain.**

1. $5 + a = 12$, so $a = \underline{7}$.
$ab = 14$, so $b = \underline{2}$.
$16 \div b = c$, so $c = \underline{8}$.
$14 - d = c$, so $d = \underline{6}$.
$e \div d = 3$, so $e = \underline{18}$.
$a + e = 25 \leftarrow$ **Check:** $7 + 18 = 25$

2. $9f = 36$, so $f = \underline{4}$.
$g = 13 - f$, so $g = \underline{9}$.
$63 \div g = h$, so $h = \underline{7}$.
$h + i = 18$, so $i = \underline{11}$.
$j - i = 9$, so $j = \underline{20}$.
$j \div f = 5 \leftarrow$ **Check:** $20 \div 4 = 5$

3. $m \div 4 = 8$, so $m = \underline{32}$.
$m - n = 12$, so $n = \underline{20}$.
$np = 100$, so $p = \underline{5}$.
$q = 40 + p$, so $q = \underline{45}$.
$p + q - 10 = r$, so $r = \underline{40}$.
$r - m = 8 \leftarrow$ **Check:** $40 - 32 = 8$

4. $18 = v - 12$, so $v = \underline{30}$.
$v \div w = 3$, so $w = \underline{10}$.
$80 = wx$, so $x = \underline{8}$.
$w + x = 2y$, so $y = \underline{9}$.
$xy - z = 40$, so $z = \underline{32}$.
$z - v = 2 \leftarrow$ **Check:** $32 - 30 = 2$

5. **CHALLENGE** Create your own equation chain using these numbers for the variables: $a = 10$, $b = 6$, $c = 18$, and $d = 3$.
**Answers will vary. Sample answer: $12 - a = 2$; $a = b + 4$; $3b = c$; $c \div d = 6$; $a - d = 7$**

**Answers**

## 1-9 Skills Practice

NAME _____ DATE _____ PERIOD _____

### Algebra: Area Formulas

**Complete each problem.**

1. Give the formula for finding the area of a rectangle. $A = \ell \times w$

2. Draw and label a rectangle that has an area of 18 square units.
**Sample answer:**

6 × 3

3. Give the formula for finding the area of a square. $A = s^2$

4. Draw and label a rectangle that has an area of 25 square units.

5 units × 5 units

**Find the area of each rectangle.**

5. 9 in. × 6 in. — $54 \text{ in}^2$

6. 14 ft × 10 ft — $140 \text{ ft}^2$

7. 16 cm × 32 cm — $512 \text{ cm}^2$

8. 11 m × 2 m — $22 \text{ m}^2$

9. 7 yd × 3 yd — $21 \text{ yd}^2$

10. 9 in. × 8 in. — $72 \text{ in}^2$

**Find the area of each square.**

11. 7 in. × 7 in. — $49 \text{ in}^2$

12. 3 cm × 3 cm — $9 \text{ cm}^2$

13. 8 yd × 8 yd — $64 \text{ yd}^2$

Chapter 1 ........ 59 ........ Course 1

---

## 1-9 Study Guide and Intervention

NAME _____ DATE _____ PERIOD _____

### Algebra: Area Formulas

The **area** of a figure is the number of square units needed to cover a surface. You can use a formula to find the area of a rectangle. The formula for finding the area of a rectangle is $A = \ell \times w$. In this formula, A represents area, $\ell$ represents the length of the rectangle, and $w$ represents the width of the rectangle.

**Example 1** Find the area of a rectangle with length 8 feet and width 7 feet.

$A = \ell \times w$    Area of a rectangle
$A = 8 \times 7$    Replace $\ell$ with 8 and $w$ with 7.
$A = 56$
The area is 56 square feet.

**Example 2** Find the area of a square with side length 5 inches.

$A = s^2$    Area of a square
$A = 5^2$    Replace $s$ with 5.
$A = 25$
The area is 25 square inches.

### Exercises

**Find the area of each figure.**

1. $16 \text{ units}^2$

2. 5 ft × 8 ft — $40 \text{ ft}^2$

3. 7 cm × 3 cm — $21 \text{ cm}^2$

4. 6 yd × 6 yd — $36 \text{ yd}^2$

5. What is the area of a rectangle with a length of 10 meters and a width of 7 meters? $70 \text{ m}^2$

6. What is the area of a square with a side length of 15 inches? $225 \text{ in}^2$

Chapter 1 ........ 58 ........ Course 1

---

## Right half (Word Problem Practice)

NAME _____ DATE _____ PERIOD _____

**1-9 Word Problem Practice**

*Algebra: Area Formulas*

**FLOOR PLANS** For Exercises 1–6, use the diagram that shows the floor plan for a house.

Bedroom 1 — 13 ft, 9 ft
Closet — 2 ft
Bath — 7 ft, 6 ft
Closet — 2 ft
Bedroom 2 — 10 ft, 13 ft
Hall
Kitchen — 12 ft, 12 ft
Living/Dining Room — 18 ft, 12 ft

1. What is the area of the floor in the kitchen? **144 ft²**

2. Find the area of the living/dining room. **216 ft²**

3. What is the area of the bathroom? **42 ft²**

4. Find the area of Bedroom 1. **117 ft²**

5. Which two parts of the house have the same area? **the 2 closets**

6. How much larger is Bedroom 2 than Bedroom 1? **13 ft² larger**

---

## Left half (Practice)

NAME _____ DATE _____ PERIOD _____

**1-9 Practice**

*Algebra: Area Formulas*

**Find the area of each rectangle.**

1. 7 m, 9 m   **63 m²**

2. 15 mm, 24 mm   **360 mm²**

3. 4 ft, 10 ft   **40 ft²**

4. Find the area of a rectangle with a length of 35 inches and a width of 21 inches. **735 in²**

**Find the area of each square.**

5. 8 ft, 8 ft   **64 ft²**

6. 2 cm, 2 cm   **4 cm²**

7. 13 in., 13 in.   **169 in²**

8. What is the area of a square with a side length of 21 yards? **441 yd²**

**Find the area of each shaded region.**

10. 10 cm, 4 cm, 3 cm, 10 cm   **88 m²**

11. 6 yd, 6 yd, 12 yd, 14 yd   **132 yd²**

12. 8 ft, 18 ft, 21 ft, 23 ft   **339 ft²**

13. **REMODELING** The Crofts are covering the floor in their living room and in their bedroom with carpeting. The living room is 16 feet long and 12 feet wide. The bedroom is a square with 10 feet on each side. How many square feet of carpeting should the Crofts buy? **292 ft² of carpeting**

14. **GARDENING** The diagram shows a park's lawn with a sandy playground in the corner. If a bag of fertilizer feeds 5,000 square feet of lawn, how many bags of fertilizer are needed to feed the lawn area of the park? **4 bags**

150 ft, 150 ft, 50 ft, 50 ft

Answers

# Answers (Lesson 1-9)

## 1-9 Enrichment

### Tiling a Floor

The figure at the right is the floor plan of a family room. The plan is drawn on grid paper, and each square of the grid represents one square foot. The floor is going to be covered completely with tiles.

1. What is the area of the floor? **252 square feet**

2. Suppose each tile is a square with a side that measures one foot. How many tiles will be needed? **252**

3. Suppose each tile is a square with a side that measures one inch. How many tiles will be needed? **36,288**

4. Suppose each tile is a square with a side that measures six inches. How many tiles will be needed? **1,008**

Use the given information to find the total cost of tiles for the floor.

5. tile: square, 1 foot by 1 foot
   cost of one tile: $3.50
   **$882**

6. tile: square, 6 inches by 6 inches
   cost of one tile: $0.95
   **$957.60**

7. tile: square, 4 inches by 4 inches
   cost of one tile: $0.50
   **$1,134**

8. tile: square, 2 feet by 2 feet
   cost of one tile: $12
   **$756**

9. tile: square, 1 foot by 1 foot
   cost of two tiles: $6.99
   **$880.74**

10. tile: rectangle, 1 foot by 2 feet
    cost of one tile: $7.99
    **$1,006.74**

11. Refer to your answers in Exercises 5-10. Which way of tiling the floor costs the least? the most? **least: tiles in Exercise 8; most: tiles in Exercise 7**

---

## 1-9 TI-73 Activity

### Perimeter and Area

Use the Equation Solver feature on the TI-73 calculator to evaluate expressions for the perimeter and the area of rectangles. The perimeter of a rectangle is given by $P = 2\ell + 2w$. The area is $A = \ell w$.

**Example 1** Find the perimeter of a rectangle whose length is 8 feet and width is 4 feet.

**Step 1** Go to the Equation Solver. Clear any existing equation.
MATH 6 ◄ CLEAR

```
EQUATION SOLVER
eqn:1 P=2L+2W
```

**Step 2** Enter the formula for perimeter.
2nd [TEXT] P = 2 L + 2 W Done ENTER ENTER

**Step 3** Enter values for L and W.

**Step 4** Solve for P.
◄ ► ENTER

```
P=2L+2W
 ▪ P=24
  L=8
  W=4
bound={-1e99,1...
Solve:P L W
```

The value of the perimeter is 24 feet.
To find the perimeter of another rectangle, repeat Steps 3 and 4.

**Example 2** Find the area of a rectangle whose length is 9 feet and width is 3 feet.

Follow the steps above, but in Step 2, enter the formula $A = \ell w$. Solve for $A$. The area is 27 square feet.

```
A=LW
 ▪ A=?
  L=9
  W=3
bound={-1e99,1...
Solve:A L W
```

Use a graphing calculator to find the perimeter and area of each rectangle described.

1. length = 7 ft
   width = 6 ft
   **26 ft; 42 ft²**

2. length = 8 ft
   width = 8 ft
   **32 ft; 64 ft²**

3. length = 9 ft
   width = 2 ft
   **22 ft; 18 ft²**

4. length = 9 ft
   width = 4 ft
   **26 ft; 36 ft²**

5. length = 7 ft
   width = 5 ft
   **24 ft; 35 ft²**

6. length = 6 ft
   width = 1 ft
   **14 ft; 6 ft²**

# Chapter 1 Assessment Answer Key

**Quiz 1** (1-1 through 1-3)
**Page 67**

1. _____ $375 _____

2. _____ $160 _____

3. _____ 28, 33, 38 _____

4. _____ composite _____

5. _____ 13 _____

6. _____ $2 \times 2 \times 3 \times 7$ _____

7. _____ $8^2$ _____

8. _____ $5^4$ _____

9. _____ $2 \times 2 \times 2$; 8 _____

10. _____ $10 \times 10 \times 10 \times 10$; 10,000 _____

**Quiz 2** (Lessons 1-4 and 1-5)
**Page 67**

1. _____ 6 _____

2. _____ 31 _____

3. _____ 13 _____

4. _____ 41 _____

5. _____ 16 _____

6. _____ 7 _____

7. _____ 43 _____

8. _____ 63 _____

9. _____ 32 _____

**Quiz 3** (Lessons 1-6 and 1-7)
**Page 68**

1. _____ 5; 7; 10 _____

2. _____ 0; 6; 12 _____

3. _____ $4x$ _____

4. _____ $x - 2$ _____

5. _____ B _____

**Quiz 4** (Lessons 1-8 and 1-9)
**Page 68**

1. _____ 13 _____

2. _____ 9 _____

3. _____ 17 _____

4. _____ 27 ft$^2$ _____

5. _____ 110 in$^2$ _____

**Mid-Chapter Test**
**Page 69**

1. _____ D _____

2. _____ H _____

3. _____ B _____

4. _____ J _____

5. _____ C _____

6. _____ F _____

7. _____ 3 hr _____

8. _____ 19, 21, 23 _____

9. _____ $10^2$ _____

10. _____ $3^4$ _____

11. _____ neither _____

12. _____ composite _____

13. _____ prime _____

14. _____ 48 min _____

15. _____ $5 \times \$3 + 3 \times \$2$; $21 _____

**Answers**

# Chapter 1 Assessment Answer Key

**Vocabulary Test**
**Page 70**

1. _____exponent_____

2. _____factor_____

3. _____solution_____

4. _____formula_____

5. _____equation_____

6. _____area_____

7. __prime number__

8. _____cubed_____

9. _____variable_____

10. _____powers_____

11. expressing a composite number as a product of prime numbers

12. variables and numbers combined by at least one operation

**Form 1**
**Page 71**

1. __B__

2. __F__

3. __D__

4. __G__

5. __B__

6. __F__

7. __C__

8. __G__

9. __B__

10. __J__

11. __B__

12. __F__

13. __C__

**Page 72**

14. __J__

15. __B__

16. __F__

17. __C__

18. __G__

19. __C__

20. __F__

21. __D__

22. __H__

23. __D__

24. __F__

25. __B__

B: _____23_____

# Chapter 1 Assessment Answer Key

**Form 2A**
**Page 73**

1. __B__

2. __F__

3. __C__

4. __F__

5. __C__

6. __F__

7. __C__

8. __J__

9. __D__

10. __G__

11. __A__

12. __J__

**Page 74**

13. __C__

14. __J__

15. __A__

16. __G__

17. __D__

18. __H__

19. __B__

20. __H__

21. __B__

22. __G__

23. __A__

24. __J__

25. __B__

B: __36__

**Form 2B**
**Page 75**

1. __D__

2. __G__

3. __C__

4. __H__

5. __B__

6. __J__

7. __C__

8. __F__

9. __D__

10. __G__

11. __C__

12. __H__

13. __A__

(continued on the next page)

**Answers**

# Chapter 1 Assessment Answer Key

**Form 2B (continued) — Page 76**

14. **G**

15. **C**

16. **F**

17. **D**

18. **G**

19. **A**

20. **J**

21. **C**

22. **H**

23. **A**

24. **J**

25. **B**

B: 23

**Form 2C — Page 77**

1. 23

2. 19, 22, 25

3. 32 yd$^2$

4. $11^2$; 121

5. $5^3$; 125

6. $10^4$; 10,000

7. $8^3$; 512

8. $3 \times 3$; 9

9. $4 \times 4 \times 4$; 64

10. $10 \times 10 \times 10 \times 10 \times 10$; 100,000

11. $5 \times 5$; 25

12. $3 \times 7$

13. 31 or $1 \times 31$

14. $2 \times 2 \times 2 \times 11$

15. $2 \times 2 \times 5 \times 5$

**Page 78**

16. 18

17. 26

18. 8

19. 88

20. 2

21. 11

22. 21

23. 126

24. $x + 2$

25. $3x$

26. $x \div 4$

27. 4 quarters, 1 dime, 1 nickel

28. 6

29. 28

30. 10

31. 15

32. 2

33. 5

B: 2

# Chapter 1 Assessment Answer Key

**Form 2D**
**Page 79**

1. _____ 49 _____

2. _____ 19, 23, 27 _____

3. _____ 96 m² _____

4. _____ 12²; 144 _____

5. _____ 3³; 27 _____

6. _____ 10³; 1,000 _____

7. _____ 4⁵; 1,024 _____

8. _____ 11 × 11; 121 _____

9. _____ 3 × 3 × 3; 27 _____

10. _____ 10 × 10 × 10 × 10 × 10 × 10; 1,000,000 _____

11. _____ 9 × 9; 81 _____

12. _____ 3 × 5 _____

13. _____ 29 or 1 × 29 _____

14. _____ 3 × 3 × 11 _____

15. _____ 2 × 3 × 13 _____

**Page 80**

16. _____ 17 _____

17. _____ 28 _____

18. _____ 14 _____

19. _____ 11 _____

20. _____ 3 _____

21. _____ 19 _____

22. _____ 20 _____

23. _____ 33 _____

24. _____ 4$x$ _____

25. _____ $x \div 3$ _____

26. _____ $x - 2$ _____

27. _____ 3 quarters, 2 dimes, 3 nickels _____

28. _____ 18 _____

29. _____ 40 _____

30. _____ 10 _____

31. _____ 16 _____

32. _____ 3 _____

33. _____ 7 _____

B: _____ 0 _____

Answers

# Chapter 1 Assessment Answer Key

1. _____35_____

2. _____$145_____

3. _____162 ft$^2$_____

4. _____168 in$^2$_____

5. _____12$^2$; 144_____

6. _____3$^5$; 243_____

7. _____10 × 10 × 10; 1,000_____

8. _____2 × 2 × 2 × 2 × 2 × 2; 64_____

9. _____1, 2, 4, 7, 8, 14, 28, 56_____

10. _____prime_____

11. _____2 × 2 × 31_____

12. _____2 × 2 × 2 × 2 × 3_____

13. _____111_____

14. _____7_____

15. _____17_____

16. _____21_____

17. _____3$x$_____

18. _____$x$ ÷ 4_____

19. _____2$x$ + 3_____

20. _____8_____

21. _____13_____

22. _____33_____

23. _____15_____

24. _____56 mph_____

25. _____6_____

B: _____$1–35 prizes, $7–5 prizes, $5–7 prizes_____

# Chapter 1 Assessment Answer Key

## Page 83, Extended-Response Test
### Scoring Rubric

| Level | Specific Criteria |
|-------|-------------------|
| 4 | The student demonstrates a **thorough understanding** of the mathematics concepts and/or procedures embodied in the task. The student has responded correctly to the task, used mathematically sound procedures, and provided clear and complete explanations and interpretations. The response may contain minor flaws that do not detract from the demonstration of a thorough understanding. |
| 3 | The student demonstrates an **understanding** of the mathematics concepts and/or procedures embodied in the task. The student's response to the task is essentially correct with the mathematical procedures used and the explanations and interpretations provided demonstrating an essential but less than thorough understanding. The response may contain minor errors that reflect inattentive execution of the mathematical procedures or indications of some misunderstanding of the underlying mathematics concepts and/or procedures. |
| 2 | The student has demonstrated only a **partial understanding** of the mathematics concepts and/or procedures embodied in the task. Although the student may have used the correct approach to obtaining a solution or may have provided a correct solution, the student's work lacks an essential understanding of the underlying mathematical concepts. The response contains errors related to misunderstanding important aspects of the task, misuse of mathematical procedures, or faulty interpretations of results. |
| 1 | The student has demonstrated a **very limited understanding** of the mathematics concepts and/or procedures embodied in the task. The student's response to the task is incomplete and exhibits many flaws. Although the student has addressed some of the conditions of the task, the student reached an inadequate conclusion and/or provided reasoning that was faulty or incomplete. The response exhibits many errors or may be incomplete. |
| 0 | The student has provided a **completely incorrect** solution or uninterpretable response, or no response at all. |

Answers

# Chapter 1 Assessment Answer Key

## Page 83, Extended-Response Test
## Sample Answers

*In addition to the scoring rubric found on page A35, the following sample answers may be used as guidance in evaluating open-ended assessment items.*

1. The four steps are understand, plan, solve, and examine. In the understand step you try to understand what the problem is asking and what information you need. In the plan step, you look at the facts you know and how they may be related. You plan a strategy for solving the problem and estimate the answer. In the solve step, you use your plan to solve the problem. If your plan doesn't work, you revise your plans or make a new plan. In the examine step, you look at the problem again. You compare your answer to your estimate and decide if your answer makes sense.

2. First you simplify the expressions inside parentheses. Next you find the value of all the powers. Then you multiply and divide in order from left to right. Finally, you add and subtract in order from left to right.

3. **a.** Use a factor tree to find two factors of a number. Then find factors of these factors and the following factors until all factors are prime.

   **b.** The prime factorization of 120 is: $120 = 2 \cdot 2 \cdot 2 \cdot 3 \cdot 5$.

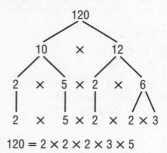

   $120 = 2 \times 2 \times 2 \times 3 \times 5$

   **c.** You know that the area of a rectangle is $A = \ell \times w$. You can set up an algebraic equation to find possible formations and then substitute numbers and use mental math or guess and check to solve the equation. $120 = \ell \times w$. Start with $w = 2$. To find $\ell$, find what times 2 equals 120. Then try $w = 3$, and so on. The possible formations are: 2 by 60, 3 by 40, 4 by 30, 5 by 24, 6 by 20, 8 by 15, and 10 by 12.

4. **a–b.**

| Input ($x$) | Output ($3x - 1$) |
|---|---|
| 1 | 2 |
| 2 | 5 |
| 3 | 8 |
| 4 | 11 |
| 6 | 17 |
| 10 | 29 |

# Chapter 1 Assessment Answer Key

## Standardized Test Practice
### Page 84

1. Ⓐ Ⓑ ● Ⓓ

2. ● Ⓖ Ⓗ Ⓙ

3. Ⓐ Ⓑ Ⓒ ●

4. Ⓕ ● Ⓗ Ⓙ

5. Ⓐ Ⓑ ● Ⓓ

6. Ⓕ Ⓖ ● Ⓙ

7. ● Ⓑ Ⓒ Ⓓ

8. ● Ⓖ Ⓗ Ⓙ

9. Ⓐ ● Ⓒ Ⓓ

10. Ⓕ Ⓖ ● Ⓙ

### Page 85

11. Ⓐ Ⓑ ● Ⓓ

12. Ⓕ ● Ⓗ Ⓙ

13. Ⓐ Ⓑ ● Ⓓ

14. Ⓕ Ⓖ ● Ⓙ

15. Ⓐ Ⓑ Ⓒ ●

16. ____41____

17. ____x = 8____

(continued on the next page)

Answers

# Chapter 1 Assessment Answer Key

**Standardized Test Practice** *(continued)*
**Page 87**

18. _____52_____

19. $3 \times 3 \times 3 \times 3$

20. _____$2^5$; 32_____

21. _1, 2, 5, 10; composite_

22. __$4 \times 4 \times 4$; 64__

23. _____73_____

24. _____x − 3_____

25. _____5_____

26. _____15 ft$^2$_____

27a. $3 \times \$18 + 2 \times \$14$

27b. _____\$82_____